A TREASURY OF
STEPHEN FOSTER

MY OLD KENTUCKY HOME

A TREASURY
OF
STEPHEN
FOSTER

FOREWORD BY DEEMS TAYLOR

HISTORICAL NOTES BY JOHN TASKER HOWARD

ARRANGEMENTS BY RAY LEV AND DOROTHY BERLINER COMMINS

ILLUSTRATED BY WILLIAM SHARP

RANDOM HOUSE · NEW YORK · PUBLISHERS

1985

CONTENTS

FOREWORD

BY DEEMS TAYLOR

So far as I know, only one song has ever made the Hit Parade eighty-seven years after it was written and seventy-seven years after the death of its composer. That song is *Jeanie with the Light Brown Hair,* by Stephen Collins Foster. In 1940 and '41, when the broadcasters and the American Society of Composers, Authors, and Publishers were feuding, the radio suddenly discovered *Jeanie.* She was sung, she was played—as a ballad, an aria, a chorus, a fantasy, a ballet, a foxtrot, a swing tune. It is a safe wager that during those two years Foster's ballad had more performances and was heard by more people than in all the years since its creation. The wonder is that it survived such mauling, that it has not departed into Limbo together with *Yes, We Have No Bananas* and the *Hut Sut Song.*

Survived it has, for it has in it the stuff of imperishability. Together with a half dozen of Foster's other songs, it will be heard for many generations to come. Just why? What is the peculiar charm about so many of Foster's songs that sets them apart from the works of his contemporaries, that keeps them alive and glowing today? For one thing, they are great tunes, true melodies. In their pristine versions their accompaniments were primitive in harmony and childishly simple in form. The radio and dance bands have brought the harmonies up to date and some of their accompaniments and arrangements are fearsomely sophisticated. No matter. Foster's airs lean upon no accompaniment. Many of them are almost more effective without any accompaniment at all. Also, they are well within the range of the average, untutored voice, without ever conveying any sense of deliberate limitation. A child can sing them; so can a coloratura. In his own field their creator, who started as a bookkeeper and ended in a free hospital ward, was a genius.

Incidentally, I don't subscribe to the popular assumption that Foster was cheated and exploited with especial malignancy. Only two persons actually exploited him: Christy, who put his own name as composer to *The Old Folks at Home* and kept it there for the life of the copyright, and Peters, who bought (or was given) *Oh! Susanna* outright and never shared with Foster a penny of the fortune he made from it. Yet even these two have a case. They drove a hard bargain, but it was not an exceptional one. They would probably have been bewildered if the composer had complained; nor is there any record that he ever did protest to Peters.

His other publishers treated him fairly, even by present-day standards, advancing him money and paying him about the same royalty that a contemporary songwriter receives. Foster's calamity was to have lived in the age that he did. The hardness of his lot has been spotlighted by the brilliance of his talent, but it was the common lot of all composers of his time (and many another since). If he found it difficult to make a bare living in his later years, one cause was the fact that out of his last hundred songs only one, *Old Black Joe,* was a hit. His average yearly income, during his comparatively prosperous years, was about seventeen hundred dollars. Today, as a double-A member of A.S.C.A.P. (which, of course, he would be), he would receive something more than ten times that sum. But that is idle speculation. We are talking of 1860, not 1946.

But to get back to Foster's songs. What quality have they that gives them such tremendous staying power? After all, other men, in his day, wrote songs that were simple, easy to sing, and easy to remember. Some of them were as popular as his, possibly more so, at the time. What was his secret?

It was, I think, that he helped to fill a gap that had always existed in our musical culture. Technically, we have no folksongs. Our ancestors, coming here from all quarters of the globe, brought with them the folksongs of what had been their native lands. These songs went into the melting pot and emerged, warped and often corrupted. They were recognizable, but they were not, and are not, peculiarly ours. It is ironic that the only race that developed a folksong literature *in this country* is the race that was brought here against its will, and was and has been the most brutally exploited of all—the Negro. The Negro spirituals and Stephen Foster's songs are the nearest to completely indigenous folksongs that we possess.

Nor is it, I think, a coincidence that most of the best of his songs are in Negro dialect and sing the woes of the Negro. A folksong is the speech of primitive people, of simple persons. It is highly improbable that the Russian Ippolitoff-Ivanoff ever heard of Foster. But it is not strange that both the Sirdar's March from the *Caucasian Sketches* and *Old Black Joe* start off with the identical phrase. Both are expressions of primitive life. Foster's acquaintance with the Negro may have been superficial, may even have been confined to the phony Negro of darky minstrelsy. Nevertheless, that acquaintance, and his choice of idiom, forced him to think in simple, clear, universal terms. And that thinking produced songs that find an eternal echo in our hearts.

STEPHEN COLLINS FOSTER

BY JOHN TASKER HOWARD

S TEPHEN COLLINS FOSTER was born in Lawrenceville, Pennsylvania, now part of Pittsburgh, on the Fourth of July in 1826. That was a most important Fourth; it marked the fiftieth anniversary of the Declaration of Independence. It was on that day, too, that the second and third Presidents of our nation died—John Adams and Thomas Jefferson.

At the very moment that Stephen was born, his father was acting as "vice-president" of a boisterous celebration in "Foster's Grove." His part in the celebration was to toast "the Independence of the United States, acquired," to use his own words, "by the blood and valor of our venerable progenitors. To us," he continued, "they bequeathed the dear-bought inheritance; to our care and protection they consigned it; and the most sacred obligations are upon us to transmit the glorious purchase, unfettered by power, to our innocent and beloved offspring." And just as the elder Foster was speaking these words, exactly at noon, a servant ran from the house telling of the arrival of another "innocent and beloved offspring." She begged that the saluting cannon be stilled lest they injure the baby's ear-drums.

Young Stephen was the tenth of eleven children, and since his little brother James died in infancy, he remained the youngest of the family. These Fosters were prominent people in Western Pennsylvania; they were active in both political and commercial affairs. The father, William Barclay Foster, was at one time Mayor of Allegheny, where he had settled after leaving Lawrenceville. The eldest son, William Barclay, Junior, was an engineer who laid out the route of many of the Ohio and Pennsylvania canals, and later that part of the Pennsylvania Railroad which crosses the Allegheny Mountains. When he died he was a vice-president of the Railroad. One of Stephen's sisters, Ann Eliza, married Edward Buchanan, a brother of James Buchanan, fifteenth President of the United States. Another brother, Henry, was for a number of years in the Land Office at Washington. Morrison, the son nearest in age to Stephen, became prominent in business and in politics.

Stephen was different from the rest of the children. He was a dreamer, and, above everything else, he loved music. He learned to play the flute and the violin, and he could pick out tunes on the piano. The other members of the family liked music, too, but they did not think that a man should spend too much time at it. There was more important work to be done in a flourishing pioneer community; music should be kept within reasonable limits as a pleasant pastime. When Stephen went to boarding school he promised that he would not pay any attention to his music until after eight o'clock in the evening.

On one occasion Stephen's father wrote to Brother William: "It is a source of much comfort to your mother and myself that Stephen does not appear to have any evil propensities to indulge; he seeks no associates, and his leisure hours are all devoted to music, for which he possesses a strange talent." Stephen's mother also tried to relieve William's anxiety about his youngest brother when she wrote a month later: "He is not so much devoted to music as he once was; other studies seem to be elevated in his opinion."

And so it went, the family always trying to make Stephen conform to the accepted, conventional pattern, closing their eyes to the talent that would some day make his name a household word throughout the world. They even tried to get him appointed to West Point, and Stephen himself suggested the Navy. Finally it was decided to send him to Cincinnati, where his brother Dunning had a commission business and would teach him to be a bookkeeper. So the twenty-year-old Stephen sailed down the Ohio, on one of the river-boats he would some day immortalize in song, far more entranced with the singing of the Negro deck-hands than with the figures he was to add for three long years.

Stephen stayed in Cincinnati from the Fall of 1846 until January or early February, 1850. These were the years of the Mexican War, and Dunning enlisted in the Army and left Stephen in the office with his partner in the business, Archibald Irwin. Stephen was a good bookkeeper; there is no evidence to support the legends that he was an idler and neglected his work. But he was always primarily interested in writing music and verses, and he spent much of his spare time cultivating the acquaintance of minstrel performers who might sing his songs in public. Some of these singers were unscrupulous and took the manuscript copies to publishers who promptly issued pirated editions. When Stephen himself found a publisher to issue *Oh! Susanna* and *Old Uncle Ned,* several other firms had already published these songs.

Oh! Susanna was probably composed before Stephen went to Cincinnati, but it was while he was there that he came in touch with W. C. Peters, a music publisher Stephen's family had known in Pittsburgh. Stephen gave Peters a number of songs, either for $100, or as an outright present, we do not know which. Peters made a fortune from them and Foster had no royalty interest. Instead, he gained from the songs the fame he needed to establish himself as a song-writer. *Oh! Susanna* became a folksong almost overnight. The Forty-niners caught it up and sang it on their way to California, and there was hardly a minstrel troupe that did not sing it at every performance.

As a result of this success, two publishers, one in New York and the other in Baltimore, offered Stephen royalty contracts and agreed to pay him two cents for every copy of his songs they sold. Now he could return to his family in Allegheny and prove to them that he could make a better living by song-writing than as a bookkeeper. He could also propose marriage to Jane McDowell and tell her that he had good prospects for supporting her. Jane was the daughter of a Pittsburgh physician who had died the previous Spring. She and Stephen were married July 22, 1850, and after a brief honeymoon in New York and Baltimore, they went to live with the Foster family in Allegheny.

Nobody knows exactly how happy a marriage it proved to be, even though the marital relations of Stephen and Jane have been used as the basis of fanciful movie plots and for radio sketches. Probably it was as happy as could be expected with a man of Stephen's temperament. Although there were several separations, one of them in 1854, it is not clear that they were caused by estrangements, and certainly not because Stephen loved another woman. In Stephen's last years Jane left him because he could not support her. Perhaps Jane was not overfond of music and had a lukewarm interest in Stephen's song-writing. It is probable that she nagged him, and that Stephen resented her trying to make him more of a businessman. Stephen was a dreamer, improvident and temperamentally difficult. Yet he was generous, sociable and lovable. He undoubtedly loved his wife and he adored his little daughter, Marion. In her old age this only child of Stephen Foster remembered her father chiefly for his constant desire that she and her mother should have a good time.

It was during the first five or six years of his married life that Stephen composed his finest songs: *Old Folks at Home* in 1851; *Massa's in de Cold Ground* in 1852; *My*

Old Kentucky Home and *Old Dog Tray* in 1853; *Jeanie with the Light Brown Hair* in 1854; *Come Where My Love Lies Dreaming* in 1855 and *Gentle Annie* in 1856. The contracts he signed with Firth, Pond & Company of New York and with F. D. Benteen of Baltimore gave him a fair income. In a little more than six years Firth, Pond had paid him a total of $9,596.96, and Benteen $461.85. In the 1850's an income of a little less than $2,000 a year was adequate for comfortable living, but it did not constitute wealth, nor anything approaching what a song-writer today would earn if his works achieved popularity equal to those of Stephen Foster. Anyway, the Fosters spent a little more than Stephen earned each year, and his account book shows debts to landlords and tailors and borrowings from his brothers William and Morrison.

By 1857 financial matters reached a crisis; so Stephen drew up a list of what each of his songs had earned, and then estimated what each of them should bring him in the future. He figured that the thirty-six songs Firth, Pond & Company had on royalty were worth $2,786.77, and he offered to sell his future rights in those songs for that amount. Firth, Pond & Company settled for approximately two-thirds of the sum Foster asked. They paid him $1,500 in cash and notes, and cancelled the amount of $372.28 which he had overdrawn on his previous royalty account—a total of $1,872.28. To Benteen Stephen sold for $200 the future rights in sixteen songs which had earned him $461.85 during the past six years.

A year later Foster made a new contract with Firth, Pond & Company in which he agreed to compose for them exclusively for two and a half years. He was to receive a royalty of ten per cent on the retail price of his songs and an advance of $100 on each song he wrote, up to twelve each year. This was a better contract, but by that time Stephen had passed his creative prime. In the two and a half years of the agreement, until August 9, 1860, he published sixteen songs which earned royalties of only $700. By July of 1860, he was overdrawn at the publishers by nearly $1,400; so once more the slate must be wiped clean. He sold his future rights to Firth, Pond & Company, this time for $1,600. The publishers deducted the overdraft and paid Stephen $203.36.

With this money Stephen settled his affairs in Allegheny and moved his family to New York, where he would be in closer touch with publishers and with minstrel performers. Firth, Pond is said to have offered him a salary of $800 for writing twelve songs a year, and a Philadelphia publisher, Lee & Walker, agreed to pay him $400 for six songs. These arrangements would assure him of at least $1,200 a year.

On his arrival in New York Stephen handed Firth, Pond & Company a song he had written just before he left home. The publishers must have been delighted to discover that it had all the warmth and richness of Stephen's great songs of earlier years. But *Old Black Joe* proved to be only a momentary flash of Stephen's former genius. During his last four years he turned out more than a hundred songs, but the quantity was not accompanied by quality. He often collaborated with lyric writers who provided him with the words he no longer wrote himself, and generally the results were mere potboilers.

The salary contracts with Firth, Pond & Company and with the Philadelphia firm did not last long; so Stephen began selling songs for cash to other publishers. Most of them were glad to have his name in their catalogues and were not too particular about the kind of songs they got, as long as they were by Stephen Foster. The cash was spent as soon as it was received, some of it for food and shelter and a large part for drink. By this time Stephen was using liquor as an escape from his worries, and had become an incurable alcoholic.

Jane tried to stick it out. When she and Marion came to New York with Stephen, the three of them boarded for a time at 113 Greene Street, with Mrs. Louisa Stuart. Stephen worked hard. He made friends with the men of his profession and he started collaborating with some of them, notably with George Cooper, who provided him with the words of many of his Civil War songs. In later years Cooper was to become famous for the verses of *Sweet Genevieve,* to music by Henry Tucker. In the summer of 1861 Jane and Marion went to Lewistown, Pennsylvania, to visit Jane's sister. Stephen lived alone for several months, and his loneliness made him drink more heavily. By this time his habits were becoming a serious problem, and Jane paid what money she could for various "cures." Stephen patiently submitted to them and made an honest effort to throw off his craving for the "rum" a grocer on Hester Street made from French spirits and brown sugar.

By September Jane was worried. She borrowed train fare from Morrison Foster, and made a trip to New York. After one look at Stephen, she decided he must not be alone, and the family again tried living in a boarding house. But it did not work. The next summer Jane went back to Lewistown, and as far as is known, she did not live again with Stephen. Since Stephen could no longer support her, she became a telegrapher for the Pennsylvania Railroad at Greensburg, Pennsylvania.

She realized that New York was not the place for Stephen, and she did everything she could to get him away and to have him join her in some place where the strain and tension would be less. In her recently published *Chronicles of Stephen Foster's Family,* Stephen's niece, Evelyn Foster Morneweck, tells how various members of the family tried to help Jane persuade Stephen to leave. Stephen's sister, Ann Eliza Buchanan, sent her son to New York with instructions not to come home until he brought Stephen with him. Stephen received his nephew with such poise and sobriety that the young man reported to his mother that he could not have broached the matter without seeming very presumptuous.

Morrison Foster saw Stephen often during these years, and he tried hard to straighten him out. He gave him clothing, which Stephen usually sold for a few dollars as soon as Morrison had left. When Morrison told Stephen that he'd be afraid of being insulted if he himself were dressed so shabbily, Stephen replied: "Don't worry, Mitty. No gentleman will insult me, and no other can." Morrison was living in Cleveland and he tried to persuade Stephen to go there with him. But Stephen stayed in New York. He had friends there who would not try to reform him, and he was still the lovable and generous Stephen he had always been. Morrison was quite accurate when he said that the drink habit was the only failing Stephen ever had.

In January of 1864, he was living in a lodging house at the corner of Bayard Street and the Bowery, then known as the North American Hotel. He was ill and suffering from a "fever and ague." He may have been tuberculous; several of the Fosters are known to have had the disease. On the morning of January 10th, George Cooper received a message to come quickly to the hotel. Stephen was lying on the floor of his room. He had risen from his bed and fallen on a piece of crockery. Along his neck, near the jugular vein, was a long, bloody cut. A doctor came and sewed the cut with black thread. Then they dressed Stephen and took him to Bellevue Hospital.

Cooper wrote Morrison, and asked him to send money. Stephen improved at first, but on the third day in the hospital he fainted while his wounds were being dressed, and never became conscious again. He died at half past two on the afternoon of Wednesday, January 13, 1864. Cooper sent Morrison a telegram which arrived ahead of his letter. So Morrison and Jane, joined by brother Henry, came to New York and took

Stephen's body from the morgue, back to Pittsburgh, where it was laid to rest in the family plot in Allegheny Cemetery.

At the hospital the warden handed Morrison an inventory of Stephen's possessions: "Coat, pants, vest, hat, shoes, overcoat." One item was not mentioned—a little purse containing thirty-eight cents in coin and scrip, and a slip of paper with these penciled words: "Dear friends and gentle hearts." Perhaps this was to be the title for a song, but whatever it was, it described quite accurately the man who added *Old Folks at Home* to the spiritual riches of the world.

The little purse and its contents are preserved today at the Foster Hall Collection of the University of Pittsburgh, together with the manuscript book which Stephen used for working out the words of all the songs he wrote from 1850 to 1860, the account book in which he kept a record of his finances, his contracts with publishers, and every known edition of all his songs. This Collection was founded in Indianapolis by Josiah Kirby Lilly and for a number of years it was housed in a little stone building on the Lilly estate which became known as Foster Hall. In 1937 Mr. Lilly presented the entire collection to the Stephen Foster Memorial at Pittsburgh, and it was placed in the newly erected memorial building on the campus of the University. And in 1940 the problem-child of the Foster family became the first musician to be elected to the Hall of Fame of New York University.

Foster composed almost two hundred songs and a few instrumental pieces. Of the songs, a half dozen rank with the world's greatest ballads; at least twenty-five of them have become American folksongs; and more than fifty are well worthy of preservation. Foster's songs fall into several types. The songs he wrote for the minstrel shows, the so-called "Ethiopian songs," were either the nonsense type of *Oh! Susanna* and *Camptown Races,* or the homesick plantation songs—*Old Folks at Home, My Old Kentucky Home*, and *Massa's in de Cold Ground.*

Foster composed many sentimental songs, many of them in the style of the English ballad that was current in nineteenth-century America. The songs he sold for small sums of cash in his last four years included Civil War songs, topical songs, Sunday-School hymns, and comic songs. Few of them have survived, and it is just as well for Stephen's reputation that they are little known today.

Stephen Foster achieved a truly American expression. Born and bred in Pittsburgh, he was not influenced by the foreign music that enslaved the composers who lived in the more cosmopolitan seaboard cities. The voices Stephen heard were those of the minstrel shows, the singing and dancing of Negroes on the wharves of the Ohio River, and the sentimental songs of mid-century that were carried through the country by the "singing family" troupes, and were sung by demure young ladies who played the accompaniments on square pianos covered with brocade and lace.

While the minstrel shows helped to produce Stephen Foster by providing a market for his songs, they were also a medium which Stephen himself reformed. He found their songs crude, vulgar ditties which struck the popular fancy, and he made into a folk-literature something that had reeked of the alley and the barroom. Foster's songs are full of the spirit of pioneers, full of the carefree impertinence that snaps its fingers at fate and the universe. Unconsciously, and without any attempt to be a nationalist, Stephen Foster wrote into his songs the subtle traits that characterize Americans.

Open Thy Lattice, Love

According to present knowledge, *Open Thy Lattice, Love* was Stephen Foster's first published song. The words, by George P. Morris, were printed in the October 14, 1843, issue of *The New Mirror*. Stephen probably read them in that magazine, and his song was published by George Willig of Philadelphia a little more than a year later, December 7, 1844. Foster was only eighteen years old when he published this music, and he dedicated his song to a twelve-year-old neighbor, Susan Pentland. This dedication started a legend that Susan and Stephen were youthful sweethearts, and that tradition has provided material for the plots of several motion pictures and plays written around the life of Stephen Foster. The differ-

ence in Stephen's and Susan's ages makes the story seem improbable, but the friendship lasted through Stephen's lifetime. Susan married another Allegheny neighbor, Andrew Robinson, in 1849, and in 1851 Stephen dedicated another song to her, *Willie, My Brave.* In 1852 the Robinsons and Fosters (Stephen and his wife, Jane) were members of a party that went all the way to New Orleans on a steamboat trip.

Open Thy Lattice, Love was successful enough to warrant at least two printings. On the first edition Foster's name was given incorrectly—"L. C. Foster." The mistake was corrected on a later edition which credited authorship to "S. C. Foster."

1. O - pen thy lat - tice, love, lis - ten to me! The
2. O - pen thy lat - tice, love, lis - ten to me! In the

[15]

cool balm y breeze is a - broad on the sea! The moon like a queen, roams her
voy - age of life Love our pi - lot will be! He will sit at the helm___ wher

realms of blue, And the stars keep their vi - gils in heav - en for you. Ere
ev - er we rove, ___ And steer by the lode-star he kin - dled a - bove. His

morn's gush - ing light tips the hills with its ray, A -
shell for a shal - lop will cut the bright spray, Or

way o'er the wa - ters, a - way and a - way! Then
skim like a bird o'er the wa - ters a - way; Then

o - pen thy lat - tice, love, lis - ten to me! While the
o - pen thy lat - tice, love, lis - ten to me! While the

a tempo

moon's in the sky and the breeze on the sea!
moon's in the sky and the breeze on the sea!

a tempo

Oh! Boys, Carry Me 'Long

Stephen once told his brother, Morrison, that *Oh! Boys, Carry Me 'Long,* and *Hard Times Come Again No More* were based on snatches of Negro melodies he heard in a Negro church to which he was taken in childhood by the family nurse, Olivia Pise. They are the only songs in which Foster admittedly used actual Negro material. *Oh! Boys* was published in July of 1851, and Foster was paid ten dollars by E. P. Christy, the minstrel performer, for the privilege of being the first to sing the song. When he acknowledged receipt of the money, Foster wrote Christy:

> I hope you will preserve the harmony in the chorus just as I have written it, and practise the song well before you bring it out. It is especially necessary that the person who sings the verses should know all the words perfectly, as the least

hesitation in singing will damn any song—but this you, of course, know as well as myself. Remember it should be sung in a pathetic, not a comic style.

Foster made a similar deal with Christy on *Old Folks at Home.* On that occasion the minstrel paid him fifteen dollars, and for the increased amount Foster agreed that Christy's name, rather than his own, should be printed on the song as its composer and author. Foster received the royalties on the sale of copies, but when the song became successful he changed his mind and wrote Christy, asking to be released, so that he might have public credit for his best-known song. Christy apparently refused the request, for his name continued to appear on copies of the song for twenty-eight years, until the first copyright term expired.

Moderato

1. Oh! car - ry me 'long; Der's
2. All o - ber de land I've

no more trou-ble for me:_____ I's guine to roam In a
wan- dered ma- ny a day,_____ To blow de horn And

hap-py home Where all de dark-eys am free._____ I've
mind de corn And keep de pos- sum a- way._____

worked long in de fields;_____ I've han- dled ma- ny a
No use for me now_____ So dark- eys, bur- y me

hoe:_____ I'll turn my eye, Be - fore I die, And
low:_____ My horn is dry, And I must lie Wha de

see de su - gar cane grow. _____

pos - sum neb ber can go. _____

Chorus

Oh! boys car - ry me 'long; Car - ry me till I die _____

Car - ry me down to de bur - y - in' groun'. Mas - sa, don't you cry. _____

Hard Times Come Again No More

Hard Times was the second of the two songs which were based on fragments of folk songs which Stephen heard as a child in the Negro church where the family nurse, Olivia Pise, worshipped. *Hard Times* was published in January of 1855, four and a half years later than the other song of Negro derivation, *Oh! Boys, Carry Me 'Long,* and its words were tragically prophetic, for it became one of the songs that Foster sang most frequently in his last days, when "hard times" were on him in full force indeed.

A journalist friend, George Birdseye, wrote two articles of memoirs about Foster for the *New York Musical Gazette* of 1869, which were widely reprinted. One of the articles contained this story about *Hard Times Come Again No More:*

On more than one occasion, in a grocery bar-room, I have heard Stephen Foster sing that good old song of his, with a pathos that a state of semi-inebriation often lends the voice; while his pockets were in the peculiarly appropriate condition of emptiness not unusual to them, and the forlorn habitués of the place joined dismally in the chorus.

all sup sor-row with the poor: There's a song that will lin-ger for-
frail forms faint-ing at the door: Though their voic-es are si-lent, their

ev-er in our ears; Oh! Hard Times, come a-gain no more.
plead-ing looks will say, Oh! Hard Times, come a-gain no more.

Chorus

'Tis the song, the sigh of the wea-ry; Hard Times, Hard Times,

come a-gain no more: Man-y days you have lin-gered a-round my cab-in door; Oh! Hard Times, come a-gain no more.

3

There's a pale drooping maiden who toils
    her life away,
With a worn heart whose better days are
    o'er:
Though her voice would be merry, 'tis sigh-
    ing all the day,
Oh! Hard Times, come again no more.

4

'Tis a sigh that is wafted across the troubled
    wave,
'Tis a wail that is heard upon the shore,
'Tis a dirge that is murmured around the
    lowly grave,
Oh! Hard Times, come again no more.

Ellen Bayne

Ellen Bayne has one characteristic which should recommend it to cheerful people; the young lady, or child, is not dead, but merely sleeping, and the song is concerned solely with wishing her gentle slumbers and pleasant dreams, and not, as in so many mid-century ballads, with lamenting her death. *Ellen Bayne* was published in 1854, on February 3, at a time when Stephen was living alone in New York.

Certain tune detectives have suggested that *Ellen Bayne* is the source of *John Brown's Body*, the song which later was the basis for Julia Ward Howe's *Battle Hymn of the Re-*

public. Their contention is quite improbable. The two melodies bear certain similarities, but they are too remote for serious consideration.

William Steffe, of South Carolina, is generally conceded to be the composer of the *John Brown* tune. He wrote it for a Sunday-school hymn entitled *Say, Brothers, Will You Meet Us*. Perhaps Steffe was actually familiar with *Ellen Bayne* when he wrote his song, for Foster's melody was probably the older of the two, but he could hardly have been convicted of plagiarism when so few of the tone successions of his song parallel those of *Ellen Bayne*.

part,   Vi - sions in num - bers   Cheer thy young heart
fear;   Love shall not lan - guish;   Fond ones are near.

Dream on while bright hours And fond hopes re - main,   Bloom - ing like
Sleep - ing or wak - ing, In pleas - ure or pain,   Warm hearts will

smil - ing bow'rs   For thee, El - len Bayne.
beat for thee,   Sweet El - len Bayne.

Chorus

Gen - tle slum - bers o'er thee glide, Dreams of beau - ty round thee bide

While I lin - ger by thy side, Sweet El - len Bayne.

3

Scenes that have vanish'd
Smile on thee now,
Pleasures once banished
Play round thy brow,
Forms long departed
Greet thee again,
Soothing thy dreaming heart,
Sweet Ellen Bayne.

Oh! Susanna

Oh! Susanna was written for the minstrel shows, and like many minstrel songs, it has served other purposes, too. Within a year after it was first published, it became the marching song of the "forty-niners" on their way to California, and today it is considered the theme song of the gold-rush and the slogan of pioneers.

Foster himself never derived much financial profit from the song, even though it established his reputation as a song-writer. According to tradition, he gave it (together with several other of his early works) to W. C. Peters, a music publisher of Cincinnati and Louisville. Some of Foster's friends said that Stephen made Peters an outright present of the songs, and others claim that he received $100 for them. Whichever version of the story is true, the transaction amounted to a gift, for Peters is said to have made $10,000 from *Oh! Susanna*.

Peters copyrighted the song December 30, 1848, but it had been issued by another publisher (C. Holt, Jr., of New York) in a pirated edition ten months earlier, and copyrighted February 25, 1848. Within three years from that date eighteen further pirated editions were printed by various publishers. In those days copyright laws were lax, and composers who were in the habit of giving manuscript copies of their songs to minstrel performers were apt to find that unscrupulous singers would take the songs to publishers and often represent themselves as the authors.

Early editions of *Oh! Susanna* are prized by collectors of historic sheet-music, and the Holt edition is a rare treasure. According to present knowledge, only three copies of the first edition are known to be in existence.

Animato

1. I ___ come from Al - a - ba - ma with my ban - jo on my knee; I'se
2. I ___ had a dream de ud - der night, when eb - ry - ting was still; I

gwan to Lou' - si - a - na My ___ true lub for to see. It ___
thought I saw Su - san - na dear, a com - ing down de hill, The

rain'd all night de day I left, De wed - der it was dry; The

buck - weat cake was in her mouf, de tear was in her eye, Says

sun so hot I froze to def, Su - san - na, don't you cry.

I, I'se com - ing from de souf, Su - san - na don't you cry.

Chorus

Oh! Su - san - na, do not cry for me; I

come from Al - a - bam - a, Wid my ban - jo on my knee.

3

I soon will be in New Orleans,
And den I'll look all 'round,
And when I find Susanna,
I'll fall upon de ground.
But if I do not find her,
Dis darkey'll surely die,
And when I'm dead and buried,
Susanna don't you cry.

Away Down Souf

This was one of the songs Foster gave to W. C. Peters of Louisville. Peters published *Away Down Souf* in December of 1848, but a year before that time the song had been the subject of an incident altogether characteristic of mid-century publishing ethics.

In 1847 a troupe of "vocalists" was performing regularly at Andrews' Eagle Ice Cream Saloon in Pittsburgh. One of the singers was Nelson Kneass, a man known to posterity as the composer of *Ben Bolt*. Stephen Foster was living in Cincinnati at that time, so when Andrews announced a competition in which a new song would be awarded a handsome silver cup, Morrison Foster wrote to Stephen and persuaded him to send a song which he, Morrison, could enter for Stephen. Stephen sent Morrison the manuscript of *Away Down Souf* and it received far more applause than any other song entered in the contest. The judges, however, awarded the prize to a song written by George Holman, a member of the performing troupe.

The morning after the performance Morrison took the manuscript of *Away Down Souf* to the United States District Court, intending to copyright it. There he found Nelson Kneass waiting to copyright a version he had made of Foster's song, and on which he had put his own name.

Con leggerezza

1. We'll put for de souf Ah! dat's the place For the
2. My lub she hab a ver-y large mouf, One

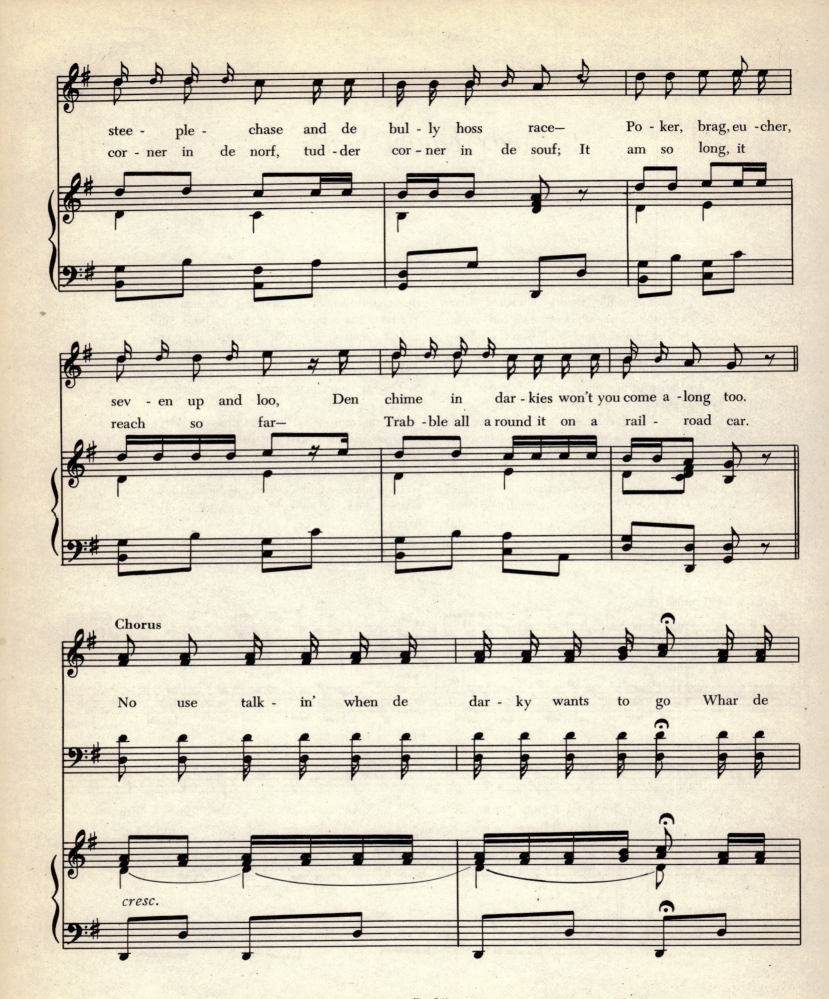

steeplechase and de bul-ly hoss race— Po - ker, brag, eu - cher,
cor - ner in de norf, tud - der cor - ner in de souf; It am so long, it

sev - en up and loo, Den chime in dar - kies won't you come a - long too.
reach so far— Trab - ble all a round it on a rail - road car.

Chorus

No use talk - in' when de dar - ky wants to go Whar de

cresc.

corn - top blos - som and de cane - brake grow; Den

come a - long to Cu - ba, and we'll dance de pol - ka - ju ba,

Way down souf, whar de corn grow.

dim.

Lou'siana Belle

Lou'siana Belle was another of the songs that Foster gave to W. C. Peters, and it was published by Peters at his Cincinnati establishment, October 18, 1847. The song was probably written in Allegheny before Stephen left Pittsburgh to work for his brother, Dunning, in Cincinnati, for it is generally supposed to have been composed for a club that met twice a week at Foster's home, and which was known as "The Knights of the S.T."

The initials "S.T." probably stood for "Square Table" and the five charter members were described in a poem written by Foster, and entitled the "Five Nice Young Men,"

which is still preserved in the Foster Hall Collection at Pittsburgh. The meetings of the "Knights" were very secret, and were conducted with elaborate burlesque rituals. Singing was an important part of their sessions, and they soon became tired of the popular songs of the day. Stephen, accordingly, tried his hand at composing songs for the group, and it was this brotherhood's need for new songs that actually started him on his career as a songwriter.

Foster's insistence upon the apostrophe in the title of this song has made singers pronounce the name of the state correctly.

Lou' - si - a - na's de same old state, Whar Mas - sa us'd to dwell; He
went to de ball de ud - der night, I cut a migh -ty swell; I

had a lub - ly cul - lud gal. 'Twas the Lou' - si - a - na Belle.
danc'd de Pol - ka — pi - geon - wing Wid de Lou' - si - a - na Belle.

Chorus

Oh! Belle, don't you tell, don't tell Mas - sa, don't you, Belle.

Oh! Belle,   de Lou'-si-a-na Belle,   I's gwine to mar-ry you, Lou'-si-a-na Belle.

3

Dere's Dandy Jim ob Caroline
I knows him by de swell,
Tryin' to come it mighty fine
Wid de Lou'siana Belle.

4

Dere's first de B and den de E,
And den de double L;
Anudder E to the end ob dat,
Spells Lou'siana Belle.

Old Uncle Ned

"The Knights of the S.T." liked *Lou'siana Belle* so much that Stephen was encouraged to write another song for the next meeting. He came with the manuscript in his pocket, put it on the piano and invited his friends to sing with him *Old Uncle Ned*.

This was one of the group of songs, along with *Oh! Susanna,* which Stephen gave to W. C. Peters, either for $100 for the lot or as an outright present, and which Peters published and copyrighted from his Louisville establishment on December 30, 1848.

Its popularity was never as great as that of *Oh! Susanna,* yet it became a wide favorite. From the drawing rooms of Cincinnati, it spread to the concert halls of the city and then,

inevitably, to the current minstrel shows.

It is said that the descriptive line of the poem: "his fingers were long like the cane in the brake," was so vivid and picturesque that Southerners would not believe that the verses were written by a Northerner who had never seen a cane brake. In 1852 an anonymous writer remarked in a periodical of the time, *Albany State Register:*

There is something in the melodious "'Uncle Ned" that goes directly to the heart, and makes Italian trills seem tame. As for poor "Uncle Ned," so sadly denuded of his wool, God bless that fine old colored gentleman, who, we have been assured so often, has "gone where the good darkies go."

Andantino

1. Dere was an old dark - ey, dey called him Un - cle Ned, He's

dead long a - go, long a - go! ____ He had no wool on de

top ob his head, De place whar de wool ought to grow ____ Den

Bass voice

lay down de shub - ble and de hoe ____

Chorus

Hang up de fid - dle and de bow: ____

No more hard work for poor old Ned He's gone whar de good dark-eys

go. _____

No more hard work for

poor old Ned He's gone whar de good dark-eys go.

2. His fin - gers were long like de cane in de brake, He____ had no eyes for to see; He had no teeth for to eat de corn - cake So he had to let de corn - cake____

Bass voice

be.   Den lay down de shub - ble and de hoe _____

Chorus

Hang up de fid - dle and de bow: _____

No more hard work for poor old Ned He's

gone whar de good dark - eys go.

No more hard work for poor old Ned He's

gone whar de good dark - eys go.

When Old Ned die Massa take it mighty bad,
De tears run down like de rain;
Old Missus turn pale and she gets berry sad
Cayse she nebber see Old Ned again.
Den lay down de shubble and de hoe.

FOSTER's songs became known throughout the world soon after they were published in America, and they were translated into many languages. In Leipzig the firm of Max Brockhaus issued a series of "Negerlieder" which included *Old Folks at Home* ("Heimweh"), *My Old Kentucky Home* ("Leb' wohl, Kentucky-Land"), *O! Susanna,* and *Old Uncle Ned* ("Onkel Ned").

The words of *Old Uncle Ned* were translated as follows:

1. War einst ein alter Neger, Genannt der Onkel Ned,
Dass er starb, das ist lange schon her,
Mit Freuden sagte der Welt er Valet,
Denn der Ruhe bedurfte er sehr.
Legt drum die Spaten aus der Hand!

> CHORUS: Hängt eure Fiedeln an die Wand!
> Denkt zurück an den alten Ned,
> Der längst seine Ruhe schon fand!
> Denkt zurück an den alten Ned,
> Der längst seine Ruhe schon fand.

2. Der Alte Ned hatte kein Haar auf dem Kopf,
Seine Wolle, die fehlte ihm sehr,
Es hatt' keine Zähne der arme alte Tropf
Und das Beissen, das fiel ihm drum schwer.
Legt eure Spaten aus der Hand:

> CHORUS: Hängt eure Fiedeln an die Wand!
> etc.

3. Der Tod Onkel Neds der bereitete Schmerz
Seinem Herrn, denn er trauerte tief.
Seiner Herrin ging's wie ein Stich durch das Herz,
Aus den Augen manch' Thränlein ihr lief.
Legt drum die Spaten aus der Hand!

> CHORUS: Hängt eure Fiedeln an die Wand!
> etc.

My Brudder Gum

My Brudder Gum and *Nelly Was a Lady* were the first two songs by Stephen Foster published by Firth, Pond & Company. This New York firm was his principal publisher for ten years, and the contract, which was signed in the Fall of 1849, prompted Stephen to leave his book-keeping job in Cincinnati, and to devote all of his time to song-writing.

Unfortunately, Stephen received no money for his first two songs with Firth, Pond & Co. His royalty interest was in songs published subsequently.

The details of the transaction are revealed in a letter from Firth, Pond & Co. to Foster, dated September 12, 1849. They offered Stephen a royalty of two cents a copy on "future publications" to be issued, but the last paragraph stated that "as soon as 'Brother Gum' makes his appearance he shall be joined to pretty 'Nelly' & your interest in the two favorites duly forwarded to your address, say 50 copies of each."

There is no reference to either of these songs in the account books and royalty lists which Stephen kept in the following years, so it is clear that Foster gave the publisher all his rights in *Nelly* and *My Brudder Gum* for fifty copies of each.

Allegretto

1. White folks, I'll sing for you,
2. Hard work all de day,

Nuf - fin else to do.   Spend my time a -
Hab no time to play,   Ber - ry fine time a -

pick - in' on de ban - jo,   Hay! _____ Brud -der Gum.
dig - gin' in de corn - field,   Hay! _____ Brud -der Gum.

Chorus

My Brud - der Gum,   My Brud -der Gum so fair, _____

All de yal - ler gals run - nin' round, Try to get a lock ob his hair. _____

3

Tudder afternoon,
I thought I saw de moon,
Saw my true lub comin' through de cane-
    brake,
Hay! Brudder Gum.

4

Went one berry fine day,
To ride in a one-horse sleigh,
Hollow'd to de old hoss comin' through de
    toll gate,
Hay! Brudder Gum.

Nelly Was a Lady

Nelly Was a Lady was the "pretty Nelly" to whom Firth, Pond & Co. referred in their September 12, 1849, letter to Foster. As suggested in the annotation on *My Brudder Gum*, Foster sold to Firth, Pond & Co. all rights in that song and in *Nelly Was a Lady* for fifty printed copies of each.

This arrangement is not altogether unusual in the case of comparatively unknown composers. It still goes by the name of "vanity publishing." Until very recently it has been the custom of even prominent publishers to offer "unknowns" a few printed copies which the composers could either sell or give to their admiring friends. Today reputable publishers, of course, frown upon such unethical practices.

The contract with Firth, Pond & Co., to which we have already referred, provided for a royalty of two cents per copy on subsequent songs. Unfortunately, no copy of this first contract with Firth, Pond & Co. is known to be in existence, but references to it in later contracts which have been preserved suggest what its terms might have been.

In spite of the doleful nature of its words, particularly the reference to her death, *Nelly Was a Lady* has for many years been a favorite song with male quartets who have gloried in improvising barber-shop harmonies to its cadences.

Andante espressivo

1. Down on de Mis - sis - sip - pi float - ing, Long time I trab - ble on de
2. Now I'm un - hap - py and I'm weep - ing, Can't tote de cot - ton-wood no

way,
more;

All night de cot-ton-wood a-tot - ing,
Last night, while Nel-ly was a-sleep - ing,

Sing for my true lub all de day.
Death came a-knock-ing at de door.

Chorus

Nel-ly was a la-dy Last night she died,

Toll de bell for lub-ly Nell, My dark Vir-gin-ny bride.

3

When I saw my Nelly in de morning,
Smile till she opened up her eyes,
Seemed like de light ob day a-dawning,
Jist 'fore de sun begin to rise.

4

Close by de margin ob de water,
Whar de lone weeping willow grows,
Dar lib'd Virginny's lubly daughter;
Dar she in death may find repose.

5

Down in de meadow 'mong de clober,
Walk wid my Nelly by my side;
Now all dem happy days am ober,
Farewell my dark Virginny bride.

Oh! Lemuel!

This humorous Negro song was issued a little more than a month before *Camptown Races* was issued, and by the same publisher, F. D. Benteen of Baltimore. If *Oh! Lemuel!* had been published several years after *Nelly Bly* we might have assumed that Foster was capitalizing the fame of the other song by introducing "Nelly" as one of the characters in the second verse. Actually the two songs were published within a month of each other. *Oh! Lemuel!* was the first to be issued, January 7, 1850, and *Nelly Bly* made her appearance the following February 8.

It is interesting to note that the opening phrase of *Oh! Lemuel!* is musically identical with the first line of *Old Dog Tray*. It is surprising, however, that Foster did not quote from himself more often. Composers inevitably re-use snatches of phrases in their songs, particularly when their product runs into the hundreds. The cases where Foster has either consciously or unconsciously followed this practice are isolated.

None of the songs that Foster published with Benteen enjoyed as wide a sale as those published by Firth, Pond & Co. *Oh! Lemuel* earned for Foster $100 in its first seven years, which is exactly $1.25 less than the returns from *Camptown Races,* also published by Benteen.

1. Oh! Lem - u - el my lark, Oh!
2. Oh! Lem - u - el my hope, Oh!

say!   Go down to de cot - ton field, And bring de boys a - way.
say!   Go down to de cot - ton field, And bring de boys a - way.

Chorus

Go down to de cot - ton field! Go down, I say! Go down and call de

dar - key boys all: We'll work no more to day

Camptown Races

Camptown Races ranks with *Oh! Susanna* as one of Foster's best nonsense songs. It is interesting to speculate on the possible origin of Foster's idea for *Camptown Races*. Musically, its refrain is similar to a Negro spiritual, *Roll, Jordan Roll*. Another old song, *Doo-Dah*, has passages almost identical with *Camptown Races*. Did Foster, then, base *Camptown Races* on a popular folk-song, or are these folk-songs variants and adaptations of Foster's song? These questions cannot be answered, for no one knows when the folk-songs originated; whether they came into being earlier or later than *Camptown Races*.

Camptown Races was copyrighted and first issued by the Baltimore publisher, F. D. Benteen, February 19, 1850. Within a few years the town of Camptown, New Jersey, changed its name to Irvington. A newspaper writer suggested that Foster's race-track song had brought the New Jersey town so much notoriety that its citizens changed the name of their town in self-defense. Careful research into the Irvington records and into minutes of town meetings has unfortunately failed to verify the tradition.

Camptown Races contains foolishness of a rare quality, and it has been popular for almost a hundred years. In its early days it was only moderately successful. In a seven-year period after it was first issued, it had earned in royalties $101.25, which represented the sale of a little more than 5,000 copies at two cents a copy. This sale was almost the same as that achieved by *Oh! Lemuel!* in approximately the same period.

Moderato con spirito

1. De Camp-town la - dies__ sing__ dis song,
2. De long tail fil - ly and de big__ black hoss,

Chorus

Doo - dah! doo - dah! De Camp - town race - track five miles long,
Doo - dah! doo - dah! Dey fly de track and dey both cut a - cross,

Chorus   Solo

Oh! doo - dah - day! I come down dah wid my hat caved in,
Oh! doo - dah - day! De blind hoss stick - en in a big mud hole,

Chorus   Solo

Doo - dah! doo - dah! I go __ back home __ wid a
Doo - dah! doo - dah! Can't touch bot - tom wid a

pock - et full of tin, Oh! doo - dah - day!
ten foot pole, Oh! doo - dah - day!

Gwine to run all night! Gwine to run all day! I'll bet my mon-ey on de bob-tail nag, Some-bod-y bet on de bay.

3

Old mulley cow come onto de track,
Doo-dah! doo-dah!
De bobtail fling her ober his back,
Oh! doo-dah-day!
Den fly along like a railroad car,
Doo-dah! doo-dah!
Runnin' a race wid a shootin' star,
Oh! doo-dah-day!

4

See dem flyin' on a ten mile heat,
Doo-dah! doo-dah!
Round de race-track den repeat,
Oh! doo-dah-day!
I win my money on de bobtail nag,
Doo-dah! doo-dah!
I keep my money in an old towbag,
Oh! doo-dah-day!

Angelina Baker

The original title-page of *Angelina Baker* stated that it was No. 4 of "Foster's Plantation Melodies, as sung by Christy's Minstrels." It was published by F. D. Benteen of Baltimore, March 18, 1850, less than a month after the publication of *Camptown Races*.

Angelina Baker is a typical minstrel song, in pseudo-Negro dialect. In the last line of its chorus it refers to the "jaw-bone" which was an instrument the end-men of a minstrel show shook like a tambourine. It was made from the actual jaw-bone of a horse or ass. When the bone was thoroughly dried the teeth became so loose that they rattled and produced a sound as loud as that of a pair of castanets.

In every sense a minor Foster song, *Angelina Baker* is nonetheless representative of the nonsense song in which Foster was so successful. One of his greatest contributions to minstrelsy was his refinement of the humor of its songs. His words were as nonsensical as other ditties, but he made an art product of a type of lyric which had belonged exclusively to the bar room. It was not so much a matter of Foster's refinements of words and music, but an individuality of style.

Foster's earnings on this song were pathetically low. In the course of seven years, it netted him a total of $16.87.

Dah's where I was born, I used to beat de whole cre-a-tion
spring-time and de tall, I've seen her in de corn-field And I've

Hoe-in' in de corn: Oh! den I work and den I sing So
seen her at de ball; And eb-ry time I met her She was

hap-py all de day, 'Till An-ge-li-na
smil-ing like de sun, But now I'm left to

Ba-ker came And stole my heart a-way.
weep a tear Cayse An-ge-li-na's gone.

Chorus

An-ge-li-na Bak-er! An-ge-li-na Bak-er's gone, She left me here to weep a tear And beat on de old jaw-bone.

3

Angelina am so tall
She nebber sees de ground,
She habe to take a wellumscope
To look down on de town.
Angelina likes de boys
As far as she can see dem,
She used to run old Massa round
To ax him for to free dem.

4

Early in de morning
Ob a lubly summer day
I ax for Angelina,
And dey say, "she's gone away."
I don't know wha to find her,
Cayse I don't know wha she's gone,
She left me here to weep a tear
And beat on de old jawbone.

Nelly Bly

Nelly Bly was published in February of 1850, at about the time Stephen returned from Cincinnati and made his home with his family in Allegheny. The song made an immediate hit, and in seven years nearly thirty thousand copies were sold. It has remained a favorite ever since.

Nelly Bly is one of the Foster songs which have became known throughout the world, and yet few of its hosts of devotees realize that it was written by Stephen Foster. In this sense Foster's songs are truly folk melodies. It is not so much that they originate with the people, but that they have been adopted almost universally as songs *of* the people and have become their own.

Nelly Bly was a reasonably successful song. It earned $564.37 in seven years. Even this much money is no indication of the wide popularity it has achieved since its publication. Foster himself had no idea of the universal favor that *Nelly Bly,* with her broom, would achieve as a household ballad. When, in 1857, he estimated the future worth to him of his songs, he figured that *Nelly Bly* would bring him about $20 more in royalties.

Andante espressivo

1. Nel - ly Bly! Nel - ly Bly! bring de broom a - long, We'll
2. Nel - ly Bly hab a voice like de tur - tle dove, I

sweep de kitch - en clean, my dear, and hab a lit - tle song.
hears it in de mead ow and I hears it in de grove.

Poke de wood, my la - dy lub, And make de fire ___ burn, And
Nel - ly Bly she hab a heart as warm as cup ob tea, And

while I take de ban - jo down, Just gib de mush a turn.
big - ger dan de sweet po - ta - to down in Ten - nes see.

Chorus

Heigh! Nel - ly, Ho! Nel - ly, lis - ten, lub, to me, I'll

sing for you, play for you, a dul - cem mel - o - dy.

Heigh! Nel - ly, Ho! Nel - ly, lis - ten, lub, to me, I'll

sing for you, play for you, a dul - cem mel - o - dy.

Ring de Banjo

Ring de Banjo was published by Firth, Pond & Company, April 29, 1851. It is one of Foster's most catchy minstrel songs, but it was not particularly popular in Foster's time. In its first six years it sold fewer than two thousand copies.

Foster could not have foreseen the kind of exploitation that would be given to this song by the radio. Today it is heard constantly over the air waves in a variety of arrangements. It is frequently used as an introductory theme for programs and for medleys of Foster airs, with the banjo prominently featured in the instrumentation.

Foster himself valued the future worth of *Ring de Banjo* even less highly than that of *Nelly Bly,* for in the 1857 estimate of future earnings of his songs, he noted that *Ring de Banjo* would probably bring him exactly $1.00 more in royalties.

Ring de Banjo was written during Foster's most prolific period. From July, 1850, to July, 1851, he wrote no fewer than fourteen songs, several of them in his best vein.

Moderato

1. De time is neb - ber drear - y If de
2. Oh! neb - ber count de bub - bles While der's

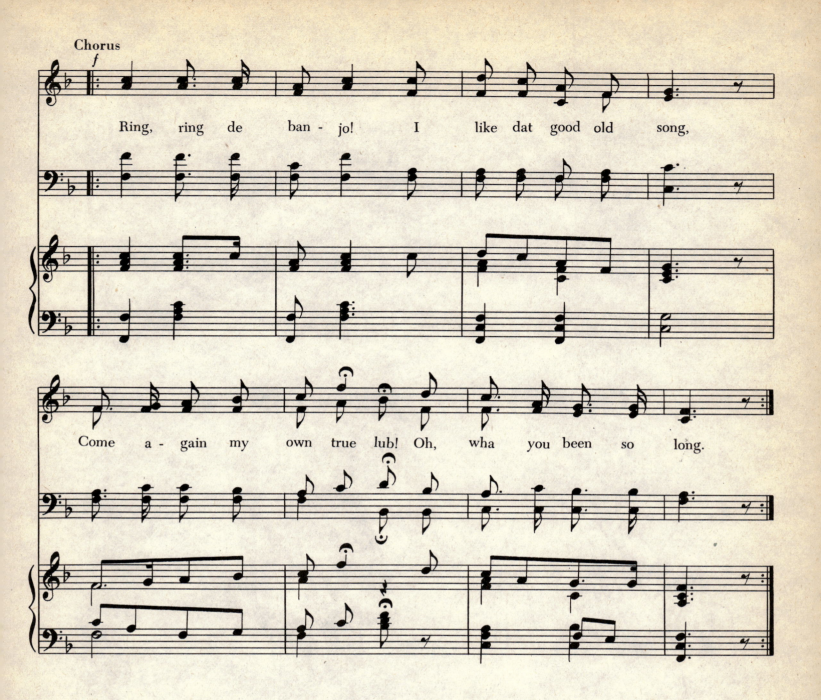

Chorus

Ring, ring de ban - jo! I like dat good old song,
Come a - gain my own true lub! Oh, wha you been so long.

3

Once I was so lucky,
My massa set me free,
I went to old Kentucky
To see what I could see:
I could not go no farder,
I turn to massa's door,
I lub him all de harder,
I'll go away no more.

4

Early in de morning
Ob a lubly summer day,
My massa send me warning
He'd like to hear me play.
On de banjo tapping,
I come wid dulcem strain;
Massa fall a-napping,
He'll nebber wake again.

Laura Lee

For eleven years Stephen Foster wrote the words of his songs in a large blank book which is now preserved in the Foster Hall Collection at the University of Pittsburgh. This book contains not only the final versions of the song-poems, but the preliminary drafts and the various polishings and refinements. At the top of the first page Stephen penciled the date—"Allegheny City, June 26, 1851." The first song in the book was *Laura Lee*, and its working into final form occupied eight pages. After the last version Stephen noted: "Sent Laura Lee,

July 19." The publishers issued the song the following August 7.

It is doutbful whether any similar manuscript book is in existence anywhere. The blank book in which Foster wrote down the words, which were to find a place in the hearts of all Americans, contains about two hundred pages on which are written both the well-known and lesser songs which Foster created during the years of his greatest productivity.

Laura Lee was published by Benteen and earned for Foster in six years only $13.12.

Moderato

1. Why has thy mer - ry face Gone from my
2. Far from all pleas - ure torn, Sad and a -

side,   Leav - ing each   cher -ished place Cheer - less and   void?
lone,   How   doth my   spir - it   mourn While thou art   gone!

Why   has the   hap - py dream, Blend - ed with   thee,
How   like a   des - ert isle   Earth   seems to   me,

Passed   like   a   flit - ting beam, Sweet   Lau - ra   Lee?
Robbed   of   thy   sun - ny smile,   Sweet   Lau - ra   Lee!

Why   has the   hap - py dream, Blend - ed with   thee,
How   like a   des - ert isle   Earth   seems to   me,

Passed like a flit - ting beam, Sweet Lau - ra Lee?
Robbed of thy sun - ny smile, Sweet Lau - ra Lee!

3

When will thy winning voice
Breathe on mine ear?
When will my heart rejoice,
Finding thee near?
When will we roam the plain,
Joyous and free,
Never to part again,
Sweet Laura Lee?
When will we roam the plain,
Joyous and free,
Never to part again,
Sweet Laura Lee?

My Hopes Have Departed Forever

Another song of blighted affection came from the same time in which Foster produced *Laura Lee*. The words of *My Hopes Have Departed Forever* appear in the manuscript book on pages between those devoted to *Laura Lee*. The verses were not, however, composed by Stephen; the published version attributes both words and music to "A Lady."

It may be that the words belonged originally to a much older song, for Stephen's sister, Henrietta, writing in 1836 to their oldest brother, William, remarked: "I have learned a beautiful new song since I saw you, My Hopes have de-parted forever, is the name of it." Perhaps Stephen made a new setting of the words his sister had sung some fifteen years earlier, but whether he actually composed the music or only arranged it, the title of the song appears in his account books, showing that he received royalties from its sale. Foster certainly was not disappointed in the earnings of *My Hopes Have Departed Forever*. His record of receipts from his songs shows that it brought him $25.04 in the course of five years. He anticipated that it was capable of returning an additional $5.00 in the future.

1. My hopes have de - part - ed for - ev - er, _____ My
2. They saw that my life was de - cay - ing, _____ They

vi - sion of true love is o'er:_____ My heart shall a - wa - ken, ah!
knew that my stay would be brief;_____ And still, though my spir - it was

nev - er;_____ There's joy for my bos - om no more._____
stray - ing,_____ I told not a word of my grief._____

_ The ros - es that crowned me are blight - ed, _____ The
_ No whis - per re - vealed my de - ceiv - er, _____ No

gar - land I cher - ished is dead, _____ The faith once con -
ear heard me sigh or com - plain; _____ My heart still a -

fid - ing - ly   plight - ed   Is   broke, and my   loved one has   fled.
dored   its   be - reav - er,   And   longed but to   meet him a - gain.

The   faith once con - fid - ing - ly   plight - ed   Is
My   heart still a - dored   it's   be - reav - er,   And

broke,   and   my   loved   one has   fled.
longed   but to   meet   him a -   gain.

Old Folks at Home

This is the best-known of all of Stephen Foster's songs, and deservedly so, for it ranks with *Home Sweet Home* as one of the world's great home songs. It is sung in almost every language known to man, and while it was composed for a specific audience, that of the minstrel show, its appeal is so universal that it has gone beyond the limits of nationalism, of race, and of time.

When Stephen Foster composed *Old Folks at Home* he had in mind nothing further than writing a popular song for E. P. Christy to sing, a home-ballad with the name of a river in it. He wasn't particular as to what river, as long as it was in the South and the name fitted the melody he had jotted down. So he started the first draft in his manuscript book: "Way down upon de Pedee Ribber." He didn't like that very much; but he liked still less the "Yazoo," he had thought of first.

So he put on his hat and called on his brother, Morrison. All Morrison had to suggest was the "Yazoo" which Stephen had already discarded. Finally Morrison reached for an atlas, and together they found the name "Swanee" attached to a river that started in Georgia and ran down through Florida to the Gulf of Mexico. Stephen, delighted, crossed out "Pedee" and wrote in "Swanee." By that act he immortalized a river he had never seen, and made it famous throughout the world.

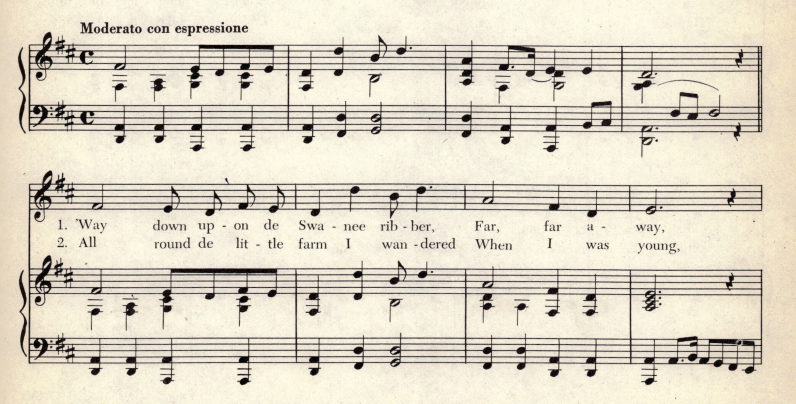

1. 'Way down up-on de Swa-nee rib-ber, Far, far a-way,
2. All round de lit-tle farm I wan-dered When I was young,

Dere's wha my heart is turn-ing eb-ber, Dere's wha de old folks
Den man-y hap-py days I squan-dered, Man-y de songs I

stay. All up and down de whole cre-a-tion,
sung. When I was play-ing wid my brud-der

Sad-ly I roam, Still long-ing for de
Hap-py was I. Oh! take me to my

old plan-ta-tion, And for de old folks at home.
kind old mud-der, Dere let me live and die.

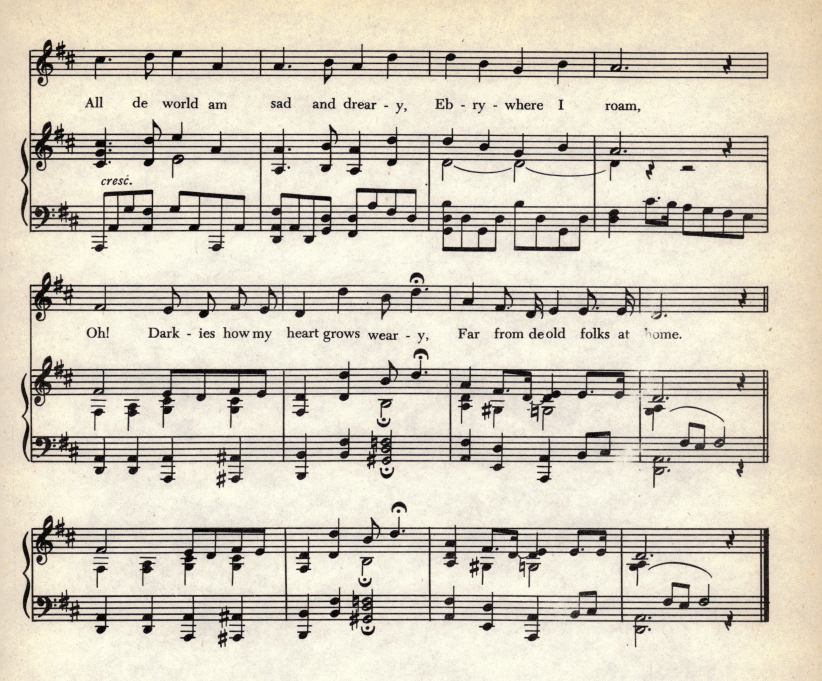

All de world am sad and drear-y, Eb-ry-where I roam,

cresc.

Oh! Dark-ies how my heart grows wear-y, Far from de old folks at home.

3

One little hut among de bushes,
One dat I love,
Still sadly to my mem'ry rushes,
No matter where I rove.
When will I see de bees a humming
All round de comb?
When will I hear de banjo tumming
Down in my good old home?

Willie My Brave

This song of a shipwrecked sweetheart was the first of Foster's "Willie" songs. Besides those included in this collection, there were also *Our Willie Dear Is Dying* (1861) and a Sunday-school hymn, *Willie's Gone To Heaven*, (1863). *Willie My Brave* was published in 1851 by Firth, Pond & Company and was decorated with an elaborate lithographed title-page executed by Sarony & Major. The song was dedicated to Mrs. A. L. Robinson, the former Susan Pentland, to whom Stephen had dedicated his first published song, *Open Thy Lattice, Love*. Susan had married Andrew L. Robinson, a neighbor of the Fosters, in 1849.

The friendship between Stephen and Susan lasted through Stephen's lifetime. In his last years, when Stephen was living alone in New York, Susan and her husband visited the city, and they invited Stephen to their hotel for dinner. Then they went to Laura Keene's theatre. Later, the Robinsons reported to Stephen's friends in Pittsburgh that he seemed bright and entertaining and apparently in the best of health. Whatever his troubles may have been at the time, he succeeded in hiding them from his friends from home.

Moderato

1. On the lone - ly sea - beat
said his bark would soon re -

shore   A maid - en fair was weep ing,   Call - ing one who
turn,   And with a kiss they part ed;   But when a year had

far a - way   Be - neath the wave was sleep-ing. _____   Thus her
passed a - way   She then grew wear-y heart-ed. _____   Oh! 'twas

sad un - chang - ing strain   Float - ed ev - er on the main —
sad, from day to day,   To hear the maid - en's plain - tive lay —

Come o'er the bil - low, Ride on the wave,   Come while the wind blow -eth,
Come o'er the bil - low, Ride on the wave,   Come while the wind blow eth,

Wil - lie my brave!
Wil - lie my brave!   2. He

3

None who knew the maiden's grief,
And saw her heart's devotion
Would tell her of the fragile bark
That sank beneath the ocean;
But when all hope had passed away,
Her life breathed forth its parting lay—
Come o'er the billow,
Ride on the wave,
Come while the wind bloweth,
Willie my brave!

My Old Kentucky Home, Good Night

My Old Kentucky Home has become closely associated in recent years with the old Rowan mansion in Bardstown, Kentucky, now maintained officially as a State shrine. The Rowans were cousins of the Fosters, and it is said that Stephen had this "old Kentucky home" in mind when he wrote his famous song. Perhaps he did, but unfortunately no documents have yet been found which establish the date of any visit to his cousins' Kentucky estate.

The manuscript sketches show that Stephen did not start his song with the present opening line: "The sun shines bright in my old Kentucky home." Instead, he penciled these words:

> Oh good night, good night, good night
>> Poor Uncle Tom
> Grieve not for your old Kentucky home
> You're bound for a better land
>> Old Uncle Tom.

Harriet Beecher Stowe's *Uncle Tom's Cabin* was first issued in 1851, and by the time Foster wrote these lines, probably in 1852, the book was fast becoming the best-seller of its day. It is entirely possible that Stephen planned to write a topical song based on *Uncle Tom's Cabin* but thought better of it because his family were all Democrats and had no use for Abolitionists.

The story told by *My Old Kentucky Home* is curiously similar to the plot of *Uncle Tom's Cabin*. In the first verse "the sun shines bright" and "the darkies are gay." "By'n bye Hard Times comes a knocking at the door," and "the time has come when the darkies have to part." Presumably they are sold to the plantations of the deep South, "where the head must bow and the back will have to bend, . . . In the field where the sugar canes grow."

Poco Adagio

1. The sun shines bright in the old Ken-tuck-y home, 'Tis the summer, the dark ies are gay, The corn-top's ripe and the
2. They hunt no more for the pos-sum and the coon On the mead ow, the hill and the shore, They sing no more by the

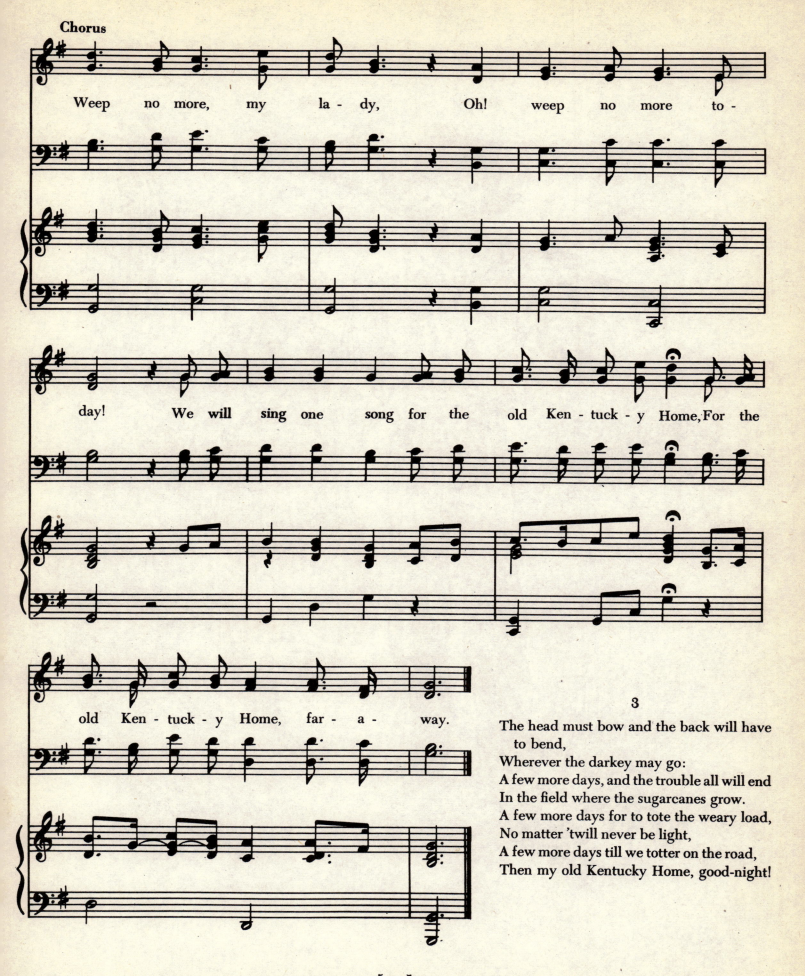

Chorus

Weep no more, my la-dy, Oh! weep no more to-day! We will sing one song for the old Ken-tuck-y Home, For the old Ken-tuck-y Home, far - a - way.

3

The head must bow and the back will have
   to bend,
Wherever the darkey may go:
A few more days, and the trouble all will end
In the field where the sugarcanes grow.
A few more days for to tote the weary load,
No matter 'twill never be light,
A few more days till we totter on the road,
Then my old Kentucky Home, good-night!

Massa's in de Cold Ground

Massa ranks as one of the "big four" of Stephen Foster's plantation songs, along with *Old Folks at Home, My Old Kentucky Home, Good Night,* and *Old Black Joe.* It was published in 1852 (July 7) a few days after Foster's twenty-sixth birthday, and its title-page bore the information that it was sung by Christy's Minstrels. Stephen noted in his accounts that Christy paid him $10.00 for the privilege of introducing the song to his minstrel audiences.

The author-composer took particular pains with *Massa's in de Cold Ground,* and devoted many pages of his manuscript book to working out the final version of the words. He tried and discarded many ideas, and even though the last draft in the manuscript book is similar to the verses in the printed copies, several further changes were made before the song was finally pubished.

Massa was successful from the start. In its first four and a half years it earned for Foster $906.76 in royalties. This amount represented a sale of more than forty-five thousand copies, considerably fewer than the exaggeration of the publisher's advertisements, which boasted a sale of seventy-four thousand copies within a period of two years.

Poco Lento

1. Round de mead ows am a - ring - ing De dark - eys' mourn - ful
2. When de au - tumn leaves were fall - ing, When de days were

song,
While de mock ing bird am sing-   ing,
cold,
'Twas hard to hear old mas - sa call- ing,

Hap - py as de day am long.
Cayse he was so weak and old.

Where de i - vy am a-
Now de o - range tree am

creep -   ing   O'er de grass - y mound,
bloom - ing   On de san - dy shore,

Dare old mas - sa am a-
Now de sum - mer days am

sleep -   ing,   Sleep - ing in de cold, cold ground.
com -   ing,   Mas - sa neb - ber calls no more.

[100]

Chorus

Down in de corn - field   Hear dat mourn - ful   sound:

All   de dark - eys am a - weep - ing,   Mas - sa's in de cold   cold ground.

3

Massa made de darkeys love him,
Cayse he was so kind,
Now dey sadly weep above him,
Mourning cayse he leave dem behind.
I cannot work before tomorrow,
Cayse de tear drop flow.
I try to drive away my sorrow
Pickin' on de old banjo.

WS

Old Dog Tray

With the possible exception of *Oh! Susanna*, *Old Dog Tray* ranked next in popularity during the 1850's to *Old Folks at Home* and *My Old Kentucky Home*. In less than four years it earned over a thousand dollars. According to Stephen's brother, Morrison, "Tray" was a real dog, a handsome setter which had been given to Stephen by Colonel Matthew I. Stewart, a friend of the Foster family. At that time the Fosters lived in a house facing the East Common of Allegheny, and Stephen loved to watch this dog playing with the children on the Common.

The vignettes on the title pages of many early editions of Foster's songs showed, strange to say, not a setter but what might be taken for a Newfoundland dog by a stretch of the imagination.

Old Dog Tray is another of the songs for which Christy paid Foster the sum of $10.00 for the privilege of introducing it. Published in 1853, at about the time of Stephen's first separation from his wife, Jane, it immediately became a favorite household song and has never lost its appeal in the almost one hundred years that have elapsed since it was first written.

Andante con espressione

1. The morn of life is past, And eve-ning comes at last; It

brings me a dream of a once hap-py day, Of mer-ry forms I've seen Up-

on the vil-lage green, Sport-ing with my old dog Tray.

Chorus

Old dog Tray's ev-er faith-ful, Grief can-not drive him a-

way. He's gen-tle, he is kind; I'll nev-er, nev-er find A

bet - ter friend than old dog Tray.

Fine

2. The forms I call'd my own Have van - ished one by one, The

lov'd ones, the dear ones have all passed a - way. Their hap - py smiles have flown, Their

D. S. al Fine

gen - tle voic - es gone; I've noth ing left but old dog Tray.

Jeanie with the Light Brown Hair

It is generally supposed that Stephen Foster was singing of his wife, Jane, when he wrote *Jeanie with the Light Brown Hair* and his other "Jenny" songs. If that is true, "I Dream of Jeanie" had a personal meaning for Stephen, for it was probably composed when he had been separated from Jane for almost a year. The song was published in June of 1854, just after the little family had become reconciled and Jane and Stephen, with their three-year-old daughter, Marion, had rented a house at what is now 601 Bloomfield Street in Hoboken, New Jersey.

Today *Jeanie* is one of the most popular of Foster's songs, but for many years it was vir-tually unknown. When it was first published it was moderately successful, and in its initial two and a half years it earned for Stephen $217.80, royalties of two cents each on 10,890 copies. Then Stephen needed cash, and he had to sell his future rights in *Jeanie*, along with those in *Old Folks at Home* and a number of other songs. After Foster's death, the copyright renewals reverted to Jane and Marion. Some of the songs paid well, but *Jeanie* brought them very little. During the entire renewal period of nineteen years only fifteen copies were sold. In 1891 the publishers paid Jane and Marion seventy-five cents, the royalties due on *Jeanie* at three cents a copy.

Moderato

1. I dream of Jea nie with the light brown hair, Borne, like a va-por,
2. I long for Jea nie with the day-dawn smile, Ra - diant in glad-ness,

on the sum-mer air; I see her trip-ping where the bright streams play,
warm with win-ning guile; I hear her mel - o - dies, like joys gone by,

Floating, like a vapor, on the soft summer air.
Never - more to find her where the bright waters flow.

3

I sigh for Jeanie, but her light form strayed
Far from the fond hearts 'round her native
    glade;
Her smiles have vanished and her sweet
    songs flown,
Flitting like the dreams that have cheered
    us and gone.
Now the nodding wild flow'rs may wither
    on the shore
While her gentle fingers will cull them no
    more:
Oh! I sigh for Jeanie with the light brown
    hair,
Floating, like a vapor, on the soft summer
    air.

Little Jenny Dow

This is another of Stephen Foster's "Jenny" songs, and like the others (*Jenny's Coming O'er the Green, Jenny June,* and their famous sister "with the light brown hair") it has given rise to the tradition that Stephen liked to use his wife's name in his songs. In *Jenny Dow* the second name is suggestive of the "Mc-Dowell" which was Jane's maiden name. *Little Jenny Dow* was published in 1862. The words, as well as the music of the song, were written by Foster.

These "Jenny" songs give some little evi-dence of Foster's domestic life. They are in a sense records of his family, notably his wife. The recollections of his daughter, Mrs. Marion Welch, who was born in 1851, about her father's methods of writing his songs were always quite vague. She does recall, however, how he would spend days locked in his room writing his music or would suddenly rush out to the music store which was kept by his friend and perhaps his teacher, Henry Kleber. Foster's restlessness was sometimes embarrassing to his family and friends.

1. Lit - tle Jen-ny Dow lives be -
2. Man - y are the hearts that have

yond the mill,   Her mer-ry voice is heard all round;   Her
sigh'd for her,   And man-y that have sigh'd in pain,

hap-py smiles are seen on the green clad hill,   Wher
Man-y that I know would have died for her,   And a

e'er the bud-ding flow'rs are found,   She greets the blush-ing morn like a
las they would have died in vain—   Lit-tle Jen-ny Dow nev-er

dew-drop bright,   And car-ols thro' the live-long day;   She
clouds her brow   In sor-row o'er a love-lorn swain: With

glad -dens up my heart like a beam of light, And
spir - its full of glee like none so gay as she, As she

drives my bit - ter cares a - way.
ram - bles o'er the hill and plain.

Vivace

Mer - ri - ly, mer - ri - ly, mer - ri - ly, Her win - ning lit - tle voice is

ring - ing And the wood - land birds are sing - ing To lit - tle Jen - ny Dow.

rit.

Willie We Have Missed You

This was the most successful of the "Willie" songs. In less than three years from the date of its publication (March 4, 1854) it reached a circulation of almost twenty-five thousand copies, and Stephen estimated that it would be good for twenty-five thousand more during the next few years.

The original edition of *Willie We Have Missed You* bore a title-page which was decorated with a lithograph showing "Willie" returning to his home and being welcomed by his wife's embrace. The assumption that the lady is "Willie's" wife is supported by a rocking-horse and drum in the lower corner of the picture. George Birdseye, who wrote several reminiscences of Stephen Foster, told of an incident in connection with this illustration. Foster was somewhat proficient in drawing, and he sketched an idea for the title-page of *Willie We Have Missed You* and showed it to the engraver. The engraver looked at the drawing and said: "Ah! another comic song, Mr. Foster?" Foster was so offended that he snatched the sketch from the engraver's hand and tore it to pieces. Time proved the engraver right and Foster wrong; it is nowadays looked upon as a comic song and is sung as such, particularly on the radio.

1. Oh! Willie is it you, dear, Safe, safe at home? They
2. We've longed to see you nightly, But this night of all; The

did not tell me true, dear; They said you would not come. I

fire was blaz - ing bright - ly And lights were in the hall. The

heard you at the gate, And it made my heart re - joice; For I

lit - tle ones were up Till 'twas ten o' - clock and past, Then their

knew that wel - come foot - step And that dear, fa - mil - iar voice, Mak - ing

eyes be - gan to twin - kle, And they've gone to sleep at last; But they

mu - sic on my ear In the lone - ly mid - night gloom: Oh!

lis - tened for your voice Till they thought you'd nev - er come; Oh!

a tempo   rit.

rit.

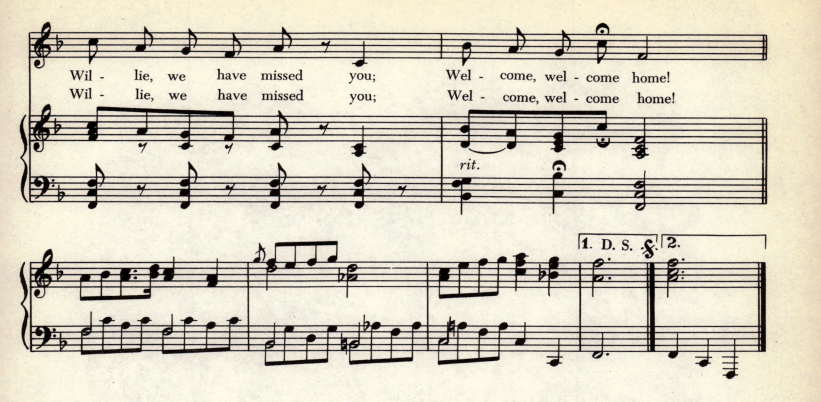

Wil - lie, we have missed you; Wel - come, wel - come home!
Wil - lie, we have missed you; Wel - come, wel - come home!

3

The days were sad without you,
The nights long and drear;
My dreams have been about you;
Oh! welcome, Willie dear!
Last night I wept and watched
By the moonlight's cheerless ray,
Till I thought I heard your footstep,
Then I wiped my tears away;
But my heart grew sad again
When I found you had not come;
Oh! Willie, we have missed you;
Welcome, welcome home!

Come Where My Love Lies Dreaming

This is one of Foster's more ambitious songs, and one of his best. It was originally written and published as a quartette for mixed voices, and it is one of Stephen's few attempts at a *"durchkomponiert,"* or *"composed-through,"* song—one which does not have the same music for each verse, but which introduces new melodic material for the changing content of the text. *Come Where My Love Lies Dreaming,* more than any other of Foster's works, has led to the comparisons that are made between Stephen Foster and Schubert. There is a distinctly Schubertian quality in the rich, warm melody of *Come Where My Love Lies Dreaming*

The song was published June 28, 1855, about five months after the death of Stephen's mother, and less than a month before his father died. *Come Where My Love Lies Dreaming* became an immediate favorite, and its popularity has continued to the present day. When Stephen was buried in Allegheny Cemetery, on January 21, 1864, the Citizen's Brass Band played the two songs its members loved the most—*Old Folks at Home* and *Come Where My Love Lies Dreaming.*

dream - ing her beau- ty beam-ing

My

Come, come, come, come, Come, come, come, come, Come where my love lies

mf

own love is sweet-ly dream-ing

(2nd time take Coda)

dream-ing Dream ing the hap-py hours a-way,

mf Soft is her slum-ber, Thoughts bright and free

Dance through her dreams Like gush-ing mel-o-dy; Light is her young heart,

rit.

Light may it be; Come where my love lies dream - ing,

Coda

Dream - ing the hap-py hours a - way.

rit.

[121]

Comrades, Fill No Glass For Me

It would have been well for Stephen Foster if he himself had heeded the advice he gave in this song. In 1855, when he wrote it, the habit of drink had probably not yet taken hold of him seriously. He was a convivial companion to his friends, and is known to have enjoyed boisterous gatherings, but he could still look objectively on the tragic consequences of alcoholism, and not realize how accurately he was describing himself as he would be a few years later.

"Temperance" songs were in great demand, and Stephen was probably merely writing a song for a highly profitable market.

The Hutchisons and the other "singing families" who toured throughout the country in mid-century were as fanatically devoted to the Temperance cause as they were to Abolition. Their repertoire included many songs depicting the evils of drink.

Comrades, Fill No Glass for Me was published November 23, 1855, by Miller and Beacham, of Baltimore. Unfortunately, Foster left no record of the royalties he may have received from this firm, so we cannot gauge how popular it was in its day.

1. Oh! com-rades, fill no glass for me To drown my soul in
2. I know a breast that once was light Whose pa - tient suf fer-ings

liq - uid flame, For if I drank, the toast should be— To
need my care, I know a hearth that once was bright, But

blight - ed for - tune, health and fame. Yet, though I long to
droop - ing hopes have nestl - ed there. Then while the tear drops

quell the strife That pas - sion holds a gainst my life, Still,
night - ly steal From wound - ed hearts that I should heal, Though

boon com - pan - ions may ye be, But com - rades, fill no
boon com - pan - ions ye may be— Oh! com - rades, fill no

glass for me. Still, boon com-pan - ions may ye be, But
glass for me. Though boon com-pan - ions may ye be— Oh!

com - rades, fill no glass for me.
com - rades, fill no glass for me.

p

3

When I was young I felt the tide
Of aspirations undefiled,
But manhood's years have wronged the
   pride
My parents centered in their child.
Then, by a mother's sacred tear,
By all that memory should revere,
Though boon companions ye may be—
Oh! comrades, fill no glass for me.

Gentle Annie

Gentle Annie, first published in 1856, is one of Foster's tenderest songs, and although it is highly sentimental, it is far from saccharine and is definitely superior to the general run of "under the willow" and "standing at the grave" ballads which flooded the song-market in these years. Morrison Foster, Stephen's brother, said that *Gentle Annie* was inspired by an actual incident which occurred in Stephen's neighborhood. In his biography of Stephen, Morrison wrote:

> Once on a stormy night a little girl, sent on an errand, was run over by a dray and killed. She had her head and face covered by a shawl to keep off the peltings of the storm, and in cross-ing the street she ran under the horse's feet. Stephen was dressed and about to go to an evening party when he learned of the tragedy. He went immediately to the little girl's father, who was a poor working man and a neighbor whom he esteemed. He gave up all thought of going to the party and remained all night with the dead child and her afflicted parents, en-deavoring to afford the latter what comfort he could.

Foster expected a wide sale for *Gentle Annie.* When it had been published for nine months it had earned for him only $39.08 in royalties, but he anticipated that it would be worth an additional $500.00 in the near future.

Andante mosso

1. Thou wilt come no more, gen - tle An - nie, Like a
2. We have roamed and loved mid the bow ers, When thy

flow'r thy spir-it did de-part; Thou art gone, a-las! like the
down-y cheeks were in their bloom; Now I stand a-lone mid the

man-y That have bloomed in the sum-mer of my heart.
flow-ers While they min-gle their per-fumes o'er thy tomb.

Chorus

Shall we nev-er more be-hold thee; Nev-er hear thy win-ning voice a

gain   When the Spring - time comes, gen - tle An - nie, When the

wild   flow'rs are scat - tered o'er the plain?

3

Ah! the hours grow sad while I ponder
Near the silent spot where thou art laid,
And my heart bows down when I wander
By the streams and the meadows where we
    stray'd.

The Glendy Burk

The Glendy Burk was one of the few later nonsense songs of Foster's which had the sparkle and light-hearted jollity of the earlier *Camptown Races* and *Oh! Susanna*. The title-page of the first edition (issued in 1860) was decorated with a picture of the "Glendy Burk," an actual steamboat which plied the Ohio and Mississippi Rivers from Pittsburgh to New Orleans.

The rivers in and near Pittsburgh exercised a great fascination for Foster. He was always close to steamboat life. In Cincinnati his brother's warehouse, where he worked for four years, was on the waterfront and Stephen could watch the boats dock. He was a frequent traveler on the river in his youth and early manhood.

Students of Foster's life at one time were excited by the discovery of the name "S. C. Foster" which appeared on the registers of several mid-century steamboats. They were convinced that they had evidence of Foster's actual travels. Much to their chagrin, they later found that the handwriting on the registers was that of Seth C. Foster, a St. Louis businessman, who traveled the Mississippi and Ohio Rivers.

Allegro moderato

1. De Glen-dy Burk is a might-y fast boat, Wid a might y fast cap tain
2. De Glen-dy Burk has a fun-ny old crew And dey sing de boat-man's

Chorus

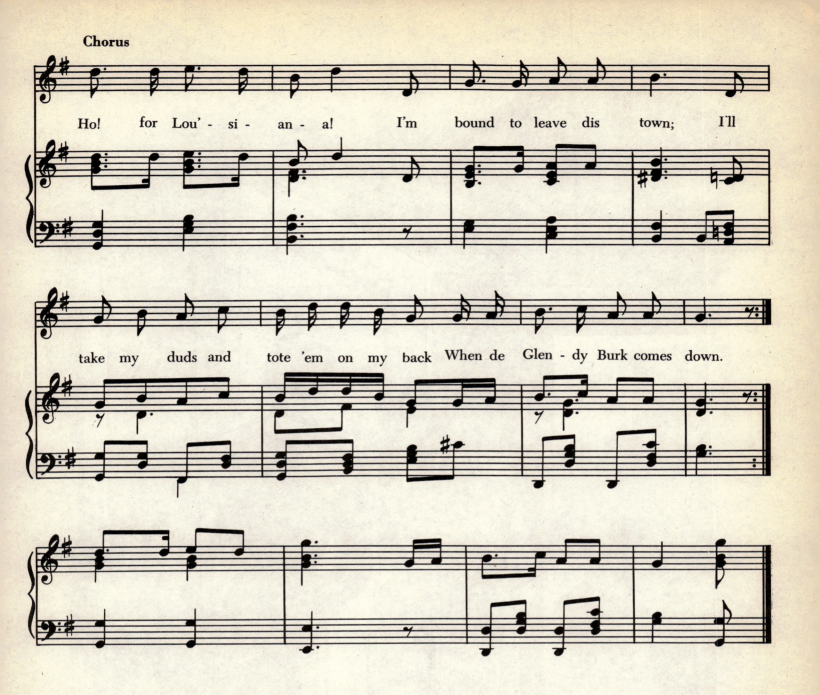

Ho! for Lou'- si - an - a! I'm bound to leave dis town; I'll

take my duds and tote 'em on my back When de Glen - dy Burk comes down.

<table>
<tr><td>3</td><td>4</td></tr>
</table>

3

I'll work all night in de wind and storm,
I'll work all day in de rain,
'Till I find myself on de levy dock
in New Orleans again.
Dey make me mow in de hay field here
And knock my head wid de flail;
I'll go wha dey work wid de sugar and
   de cane
And roll on de cotton bale.

4

My lady love is as pretty as a pink,
I'll meet her on de way;
I'll take her back to de sunny old south
And dah I'll make her stay.
So don't you fret my honey, dear
Oh! don't you fret Miss Brown;
I'll take you back 'fore de middle of
   de week
When de Glendy Burk comes down .

Old Black Joe

With the possible exception of *Beautiful Dreamer, Old Black Joe* was the last of the truly great songs that Stephen Foster produced. It was published November 8, 1860, and was probably written before Stephen had left the Pittsburgh district and moved to New York. Foster's granddaughter, Mrs. A. D. Rose, claimed that "Joe" was a real person, a servant in the home of Jane McDowell in the days when Stephen was courting her. Up to the time of Dr. McDowell's death, Joe drove Jane's father on his rounds. He also had some household duties, such as admitting visitors in the evenings. "All through the sweetheart days,"

Mrs. Rose explained in a newspaper article, "Joe watched Foster come and go, presenting his and other admirers' bouquets to 'Miss Jenny' with much shuffling of feet and many broad grins."

According to Mrs. Rose, Stephen promised Joe that he would put him into a song. And, Mrs. Rose added, "with Foster, a promise was a promise. The old man was gone when the day of inspiration came, but today and perhaps always, Old Black Joe lives again."

Of Foster's "Ethiopian songs," *Old Black Joe* deservedly remains to this day one of the "big four."

Poco Adagio

1. Gone are the days when my heart was young and gay,
2. Why do I weep when my heart should feel no pain,

Gone are my friends from the cot-ton fields a-way,
Why do I sigh that my friends come not a-gain,

Gone from the earth to a bet-ter land I know, I
Griev - ing for forms now de - part - ed long a - go? I

hear their gen - tle voic - es call - ing "Old Black Joe."
hear their gen - tle voic - es call - ing "Old Black Joe."

Chorus

I'm com - ing, I'm com - ing, for my head is bend - ing low: I

hear those gen - tle voic - es call - ing "Old Black Joe."

3

Where are the hearts once so happy and
so free,
The children so dear that I held upon
my knee?
Gone to the shore where my soul has
longed to go.
I hear their gentle voices calling "Old
Black Joe."

Down Among the Cane Brakes

This song was published by Firth, Pond & Company in 1860, one week after the same firm had issued *Old Black Joe*. Both songs were probably written in Allegheny, for their texts appear on adjacent pages in the back of the manuscript book which Foster used for eleven years, and which he left in Allegheny when he moved to New York in the summer of 1860. It is interesting to note that this "plantation song," like *Old Black Joe*, is not written in Negro dialect. Foster had dropped the pseudo-Negro accents he used in his early "Ethiopian songs"

and he was putting into the mouths of his darkies formal and correct English.

In Foster's time there was a great vogue for Negro dialect songs. Almost foreseeing the tendency to abandon in our own day such travesty on the speech of a people, he gradually dropped the use of Negro dialect, and in his later songs it is significantly and prophetically absent. It is perhaps worthy of comment that Foster came to this conclusion quite independently and was not urged to it by the pressure of any organized group.

Moderato

con espressione

1. Once I could laugh and play, When in life's ear - ly day;
2. Yes I was free from care; All was bright sum - mer there;

Then   I   was   far - a - way,   Down a - mong the cane-brakes.
Dark   days   to   me   were   fair,   Down a - mong the cane-brakes.

Chorus

Down   a - mong   the   cane - brakes   on   the   Mis - sis - sip - pi   shore,

Oh!   Those   hap - py   days,   those   hap - py   days   are   o'er!

[140]

Oh   Those hap - py days will   come back no more!

3

There lived my mother dear
(Gone from this world I fear);
There rang our voices clear,
Down among the canebrakes.

4

There lived a lovely one,
Who, like the rest, has gone;
She might have been my own,
Down among the canebrakes.

5

Long years have glided by
Since then I breathed each sigh;
May I return to die,
Down among the canebrakes.

That's What's the Matter

During the Civil War Stephen Foster was passing his last days in New York, and like the song-smiths in the Tin-Pan Alleys of all war periods, he turned out dozens of hastily written war songs.

Interesting chiefly for their historical value, the songs of this genre meant far more to the Civil War generation than they can for our own. Most of them were probably sold outright for small amounts of cash, for during these years Foster no longer had royalty contracts with the leading publishers.

Many of these songs are filled with topical allusions. One was *That's What's the Matter,* published in 1862 as "Dan Bryant's Celebrated Song," and as "sung by him with great success." This song contains references to many of the events that had occurred: to the hope of Southerners that the North would not be united; to the Merrimac and Monitor, and to Captain Ericsson. There were even such specific references to current politics as the Southern hope that the Democrats would align themselves with the cause of the Confederacy.

1. We live in hard and stir - ing times, Too
2. Oh! yes, we thought our neigh - bors true, In -

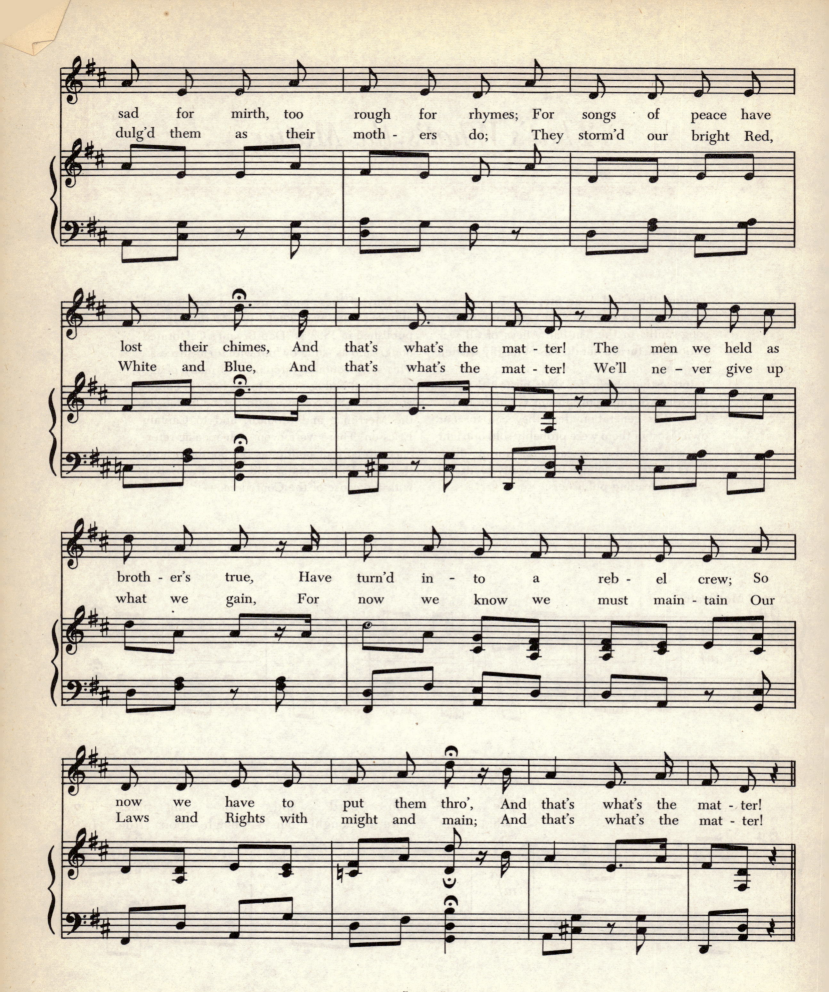

sad   for   mirth, too   rough   for   rhymes; For   songs   of   peace   have
dulg'd   them   as   their   moth - ers   do;   They   storm'd   our   bright   Red,

lost   their   chimes,   And   that's   what's   the   mat - ter!   The   men   we   held   as
White   and   Blue,   And   that's   what's   the   mat - ter!   We'll   ne – ver   give   up

broth - er's   true,   Have   turn'd   in - to   a   reb - el   crew;   So
what   we   gain,   For   now   we   know   we   must   main - tain   Our

now   we   have   to   put   them   thro',   And   that's   what's   the   mat - ter!
Laws   and   Rights   with   might   and   main;   And   that's   what's   the   mat - ter!

Chorus

That's what's the mat - ter, The reb - els have to scat - ter; We'll

make them flee, By land and sea, And that's what's the mat - ter!

3

The rebels thought that we would divide,
And Democrats would take their side;
They then would let the Union slide,
And that's what's the matter!
But, when the war had once begun,
All party feeling soon was gone;
We join'd as brothers, ev'ry one!
And that's what's the matter!

4

The Merrimac, with heavy sway,
Had made our Fleet an easy prey—
The Monitor got in the way,
And that's what's the matter!
So health to Captain Ericsson,
I cannot tell all he has done,
I'd never stop when once begun,
And that's what's the matter!

We are Coming Father Abraam, 300,000 More

When this song was published, in 1862, the title-page read: "Music composed by Stephen C. Foster." No authorship was given for the words, and Foster may not have known that they were written by James Sloane Gibbons, an Abolitionist writer, who published them soon after Lincoln issued a call for an additional three hundred thousand troops. For many years the verses were widely attributed to William Cullen Bryant, who finally issued a public denial of authorship. Others than Stephen Foster set the words to music, and when financial troubles became a problem to the government and additional paper currency was authorized, a parodist published an inflation song based on both the Gibbons poem and on Foster's song, *That's What's the Matter*. The words of the parody began:

> We are coming Father Abram
> One hundred thousand more
> Five hundred presses printing us
> From morn till night is o'er: etc. etc.

And the chorus:

> With our promise to pay
> "How are you, Secretary Chase?"
> Promise to pay,
> Oh, dat's what's de matter.

Mis - sis - sip - pi's   wind - ing stream and   from New Eng - land's   shore;   We
mov - ing lines of   ris - ing dust your   vi - sion may des - cry;   And

leave our plows and   work - shops, our   wifes and chil - dren dear,   With
now the wind an   in - stant tears the   cloud - y veil aside,   And

hearts too full for   ut - ter - ance, with   but a si - lent   tear;   We
floats a - loft our   spang - led flag in   glor - ry and in   pride;   And

dare not look be - hind   us but   stead - fast - ly be - fore,   We are
bay' - nets in the   sun - light gleam, and   bands brave mu - sic pour,   We are

com - ing, Fa - ther A bra - am, three hun - dred thou - sand more.

com - ing Fa - ther A bra - am, three hun - dred thou - sand more.

Chorus

We are com - ing, com - ing our un - ion to re - store. We are

com - ing, Fa - ther A bra - am, three hun - dred thou - sand more.

Willie Has Gone to the War

This is one song of the "Willie" series to which Foster did not write the words. George Cooper was the author and in his reminiscences he told a story which is typical of the hand-to-mouth existence Stephen lived in his last years. Harold V. Milligan, in his biography of Stephen Foster,° recounted the incident as Cooper had told it to him:

These songs [those written by Foster and Cooper] they sold for whatever they could get for them, which was never very much. The song, *Willie Has Gone to the War*, was written one morning, and after it was finished, Stephen rolled it up and tucking it under his arm, said, "Where shall we put this one?" Cooper says that he remembers it was a cold, raw, winter day, snow falling drearily, and the pavements covered with slush. Stephen's shoes had holes in them and he had no overcoat, but he seemed oblivious to discomfort and misery. As the author and composer proceeded up Broadway they passed Wood's Music Hall, and the proprietor, standing in the lobby, hailed them as they passed with the question, "What have you got there, Steve?" The song was sold then and there, Wood paying $10 cash, $15 more to be paid at the box-office that evening.

The title-page of *Willie Has Gone to the War* confirms this story; it reads: "Composed for & sung by Wood's Minstrels. 514 Broadway, New York."

° *Stephen Collins Foster, a Biography*, by Harold Vincent Milligan. New York, 1920. G. Schirmer.

Con spirito

mf

1. The
2. 'Twas

mf

blue - bird is sing - ing his lay, To all the sweet flow'rs of the
here, where the li - ly bells grow, I last saw his no - ble young

dale, The wild bee is roam - ing at play, And
face, And now while he's gone to the foe, Oh!

soft is the sigh of the gale; I stray by the brook - side a
dear - ly I love the old place; The whis - per - ing wa - ters re -

dim.

p

lone, Where oft we have wan - der'd be - fore, And
peat The name that I love o'er and o'er, And

cresc.

mf

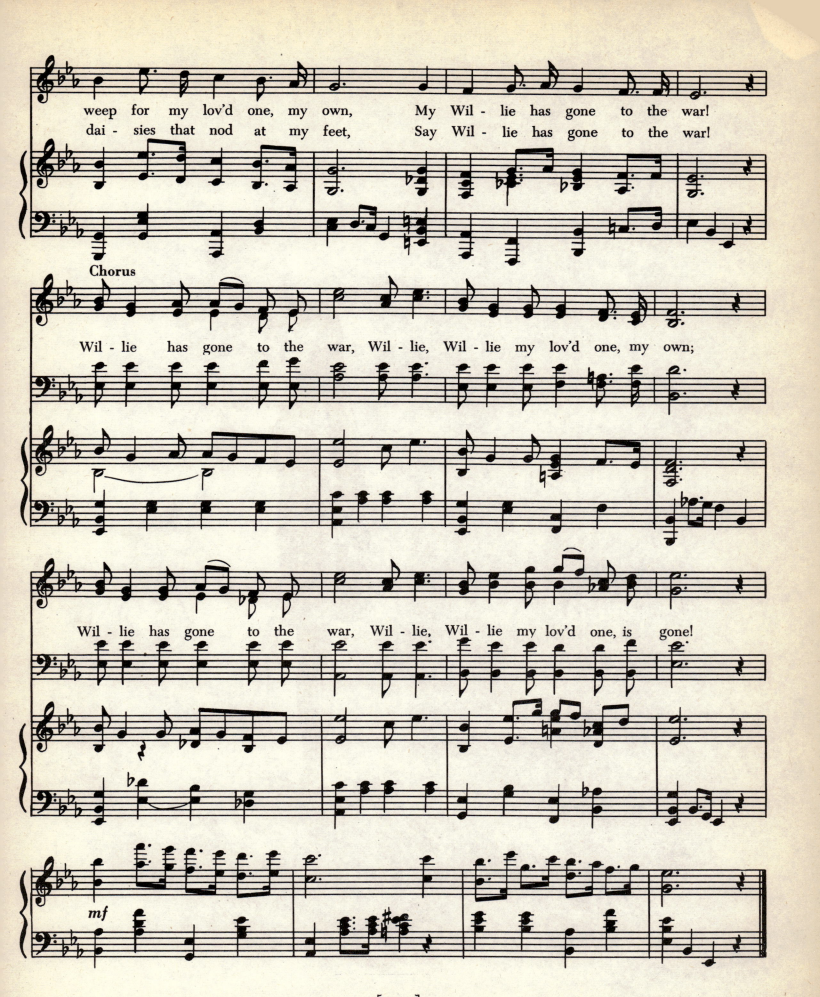

weep for my lov'd one, my own, My Wil - lie has gone to the war!
dai - sies that nod at my feet, Say Wil - lie has gone to the war!

Chorus

Wil - lie has gone to the war, Wil - lie, Wil - lie my lov'd one, my own;

Wil - lie has gone to the war, Wil - lie, Wil - lie my lov'd one, is gone!

mf

Our Bright Summer Days Are Gone

The words of this song are tragic in their implications, for they were written at a time when Stephen Foster was definitely on the decline. He must have felt the truth of his prophecy: "Never more will come those happy, happy hours, Whiled away in life's young dawn."

John Mahon, a friend of Stephen's in his later years, told about this song in an article of reminiscences published in 1877 in the *New York Clipper:*

> Stephen composed most of his latest songs in my rooms, in Henry Street. One of these, and a most beautiful one, *Our Bright Summer Days are Gone,* he took to Pond, who refused it for some reason or other and it made him feel very despondent; for about this time Lee & Walker [a Philadelphia publisher] had ceased employing him because of hard times. I was then "under the weather" myself, and I remember one evening when we were both pretty "hard up" indeed, neither of us had a cent, and I had a family besides, suddenly he sat down at the piano.
>
> "John," he said, "I haven't time to write a new song, but I think I can write 'Our Bright Summer Days Are Gone' from memory.
>
> "Take this around to Daly," he said, "and take what he will give you."
>
> Mr. John J. Daly was then my publisher, and was at 419 Grand Street. I took the song to Mr. Daly. He was proud to get a song from Foster. He tried it over and it was really beautiful. He offered a sum, which, though not a tithe of what Foster got in his better days, was still considered very handsome.

Mahon's story is substantiated by the printed copy of the song which bears the imprint of "John J. Daly, 419 Grand." The music was entered for copyright June 4, 1861.

Moderato con espressione

1. I re-mem-ber the days of our youth and love, When we
2. I re-mem-ber the flow'rs that we cull'd by day, And the

sat 'neath the green oak tree; When thy smiles were bright as the
vows that we made by night; I re-mem-ber the brook where we

skies a - bove, And thy voice made mu - sic un - to me.
loved to stray In the by - gone days of our de - light.

Chorus

Nev - er more will come those hap - py, hap - py hours, Whiled a -

way in life's young dawn; Nev - er more we'll roam thro'

pleas ures' sun - ny bow'rs, For our bright, bright sum-mer days are gone.

3

How we joyed when we met, and griev'd
   to part,
How we sighed when the night came on;
How I longed for thee in my dreaming
   heart,
Till the first fair coming of the dawn.

Beautiful Dreamer

This song is popularly supposed to have been the last that Stephen Foster composed. The tradition began with the publisher's statement, on the title-page of the original edition, that it was "the last song ever written by Stephen C. Foster, composed but a few days previous to his death." In making this claim, the publishers were guilty of a deliberate misstatement, for incontrovertible evidence shows that the manuscript of the song had been in their possession for at least two years before Foster's death.

Careful examination of the first edition, which was actually entered for copyright March 10, 1864 (two months after Foster's death), shows that the copyright notice at the bottom of the first page of music is dated 1862. Further, in July of 1863, when the same publishers (Firth, Pond & Company) issued Foster's *Willie Has Gone to the War*, they an-

nounced on the title-page that it was composed by the author of *Beautiful Dreamer*. These facts indicate that Firth, Pond & Company actually bought *Beautiful Dreamer* from Foster in 1862, and had the plates for the song engraved. For some reason they did not issue the song at that time, but when they subsequently published *Willie Has Gone to the War* they overlooked the fact that *Beautiful Dreamer* had not been issued, and mentioned it on the title-page of the "Willie" song. After Foster's death (January 13, 1864) other publishers began to turn out "last songs" by Foster, so Firth, Pond & Company, who had been Stephen's principal publishers in his best years, apparently decided that they too must have a last song. Since *Beautiful Dreamer* was already engraved, they issued it in a hurry, and shamelessly announced it as his last work.

Star - light and dew - drops are wait - ing for thee; _____
Mer - maids are chaunt - ing the wild lo - re - lie; _____

Sounds of the rude world heard in the day, _____
O - ver the stream - let va - pors are borne, _____

Lull'd by the moon - light have all pass'd a - way! _____
Wait - ing to fade at the bright com - ing morn. _____

Beau - ti - ful dream - er, queen of my song, ____ List while I woo thee with
Beau - ti - ful dream - er, beam on my heart, ____ E'en as the morn on the

soft mel - o - dy;_____ Gone are the cares of life's bus - y throng_____
stream - let and sea;_____ Then will all clouds of sor - row de - part,_____

Beau - ti - ful dréam - er, a - wake un - to me!_____
Beau - ti - ful dream - er a - wake un - to me!_____

Beau - ti - ful dréam - er, a - wake un - to me!_____
Beau - ti - ful dream - er a - wake un - to me!_____

a tempo

Dearer Than Life!

This is a posthumous Foster song, published in the February, 1869, issue of *Demorest's Magazine,* where it appeared between pages devoted to illustrations of the "Latest Style of Spring Walking-Costumes for March, 1869," and the "Latest Style of Street and Ball Costumes" for the same year. The words of *Dearer Than Life!* were written by George Cooper, who had been Foster's collaborator and close friend in the years before his death. Cooper attached the following note to the song as it was published in the magazine:

As there have been numerous songs published since the death of the lamented composer, Stephen Collins Foster, as posthumous compositions, which were not genuine, but frauds upon a credulous public, I deem it necessary, and desire, to state the manner in which the melody of "Dearer Than Life" came into my possession. Some three weeks before his death, Mr. Foster called upon me, and, as was usual with him, commenced improvising on the piano during a social chat, and, dotting down this melody, presented it to me as a memento of our friendship. I have treasured it as such; but, feeling that the public had a right to *any* composition of their favorite song-writer, I have endeavored to express the sentiment of the melody in the words hereto, and present it to the readers of Demorest's Magazine.

It was obviously more for love of Foster than objective appraisal of this melody that led Cooper to make so generous a statement.

Moderato

1. Sweet is the breath of the
2. Tell me you love me a-

fair, dew - y morn, _____ Sweet is the Spring when the ros - es are
gain and a - gain! _____ Part - ed from thee, oh! the wear - i - some

born, _____ Dear is the light of the eyes that we love, _____ Dear is our
pain! _____ Morn has no beau - ty to e - qual thy face, _____ Spring has no

wel - come when home - ward we rove; _____ Dear - er, still dear - er, in
lil - ies to e - qual thy grace! _____ Dear to me ev - er, in

joy or in strife, ___ Dear - er than all art thou, dear - er than life! _____
joy or in strife, ___ Dear - er than all art thou, dear - er than life! _____

Ah! May the Red Rose Live Alway

This is a little-known Foster song which seems worthy of preservation and more frequent performance. Stephen wrote both its words and music, and the lines: "Why should the beautiful ever weep? Why should the beautiful die?", show that when he was at his best he was as good a poet as he was a melodist.

The song was published by F. D. Benteen of Baltimore in April of 1850. It was unfortunately never very successful; the royalties paid to Foster over a period of seven years amounted to only $8.12, representing a total sale of a little over four hundred copies.

This sentimental song reflects in a measure Foster's state of mind while he was courting Jane McDowell. It was published three months before their marriage. Certainly the questions he asks in it are in a sense characteristic of a lover's melancholy, and convey his mood of longing and uncertainty. It may even have been the means by which he expressed his despair about the progress of his courtship, especially since Jane was being wooed at the time by a rival, Richard Cowan.

Lento

Ah! may the red rose live alway, To smile upon earth and
Long may the dai - sies dance the field, Frol - ick - ing far and

sky! _____ Why should the beau-ti-ful ev er weep?
near! _____ Why should the in-no-cent hide their heads?

Why should the beau-ti-ful die? _____ Lend-ing a charm to
Why should the in-no-cent fear? _____ Spread-ing their pet-als in

cresc.

ev-'ry ray That falls on her cheeks of light, _____
mute de-light When morn in its ra-diance breaks, _____

Giv-ing the zeph-yr kiss for kiss, And nurs-ing the dew-drop
Keep-ing a flo-ral fes-ti-val Till the night-lov-ing prim-rose

cresc.

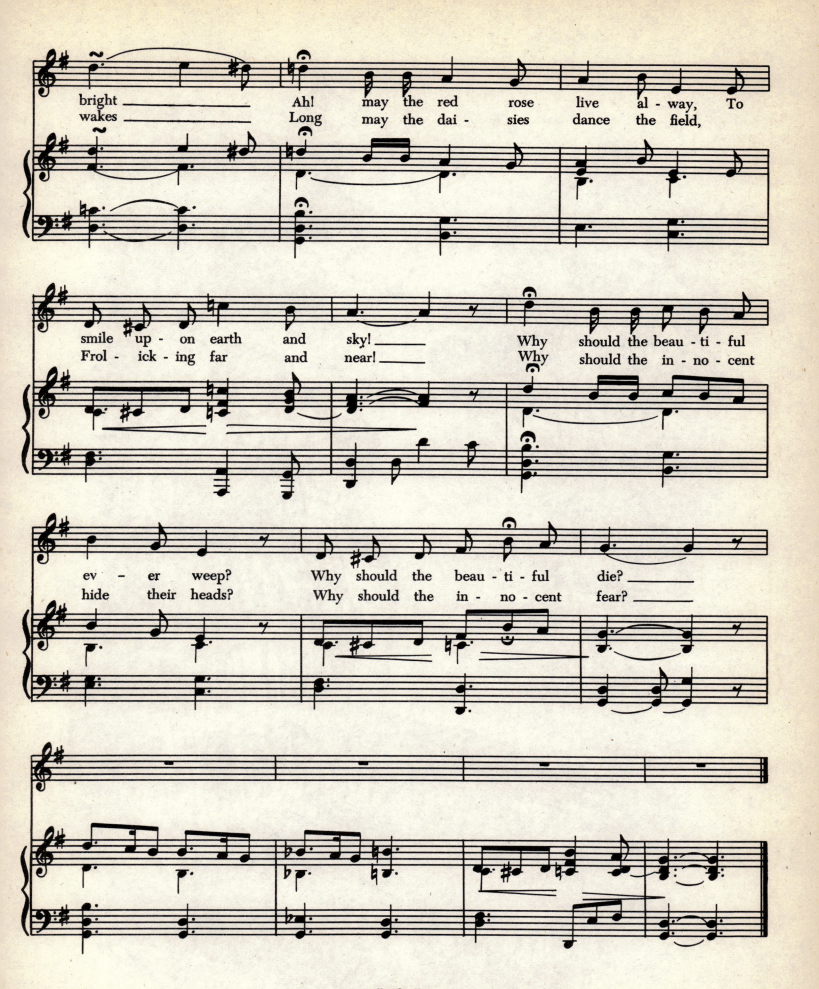

bright _____ Ah! may the red rose live al - way, To
wakes _____ Long may the dai - sies dance the field,

smile up - on earth and sky! _____ Why should the beau - ti - ful
Frol - ick - ing far and near! _____ Why should the in - no - cent

ev - er weep? Why should the beau - ti - ful die? _____
hide their heads? Why should the in - no - cent fear? _____

Once I Loved Thee, Mary Dear

Foster wrote only the music of this song; the words were by William Cullen Crookshank. It was published in April of 1851, a couple of weeks before the birth of Foster's daughter, Marion. It was never a well-known song, and in 1857, when Stephen compiled the list of royalties he had received, he put *Once I Loved Thee* at the bottom, with the smallest amount in the record—$8.00.

Youth's melancholy was often a favorite song mood with Foster. In his selection of this poem as a setting for his music, he shows again a predilection for gentle sadness.

> Youth will flee and age will come,
> Slowly, slowly;
> Death will beat its muffled drum,
> Lowly, lowly . . .

More than a manifestation of the spirit of reminiscent longing of the time, it expresses a personal sorrow that came in time to shadow Foster's later life. Songs like this are more of a portent than an indication of his state of mind at the moment of writing.

1. Once I__ loved thee, Ma-ry dear, O how ____ tru - ly!
2. I loved thee, when in ear - ly youth Love-ly ____ ev - er—

As the __ dew-drop bright and clear, Born __ but __ new-ly,
Vir - tu - ous pride and hon-est truth Neer_ could _ sev - er,

Spar - kling in the so-lar rays, To the rose-bud's beau-ty pays
And thy heart was pure and bright As the ear - ly morn-ing's light,

Trib - ute du - ly, Trib - ute du - ly. __
Sin - ning nev - er, Sin - ning nev - er. __

Once I loved thee, Ma-ry dear, O how tru - ly!
Once I loved thee, Ma-ry dear, O how tru - ly!

Once I loved thee, Ma-ry dear, O how tru - ly!
Once I loved thee, Ma-ry dear, O how tru - ly!

3

O that dream hath passed away,
Passed full sadly!
Like a genial summer day,
Glowing gladly;
And the tale of life is told,
Passions blighted, withered, cold—
Madly, madly,
Madly, madly.
Once I loved thee, Mary dear,
O how truly!
Once I loved thee, Mary dear,
O how truly!

4

Once I loved thee, Mary dear—
Still, God bless thee!
May ever blissful prospects cheer
And joy caress thee;
Though I drain my cups apart,
May, like mine, a saddened heart
Ne'er distress thee—
Once I loved thee, Mary dear,
O how truly!
Once I loved thee, Mary dear,
O how truly!

5

Youth will fleet, and age will come,
Slowly, slowly;
Death will beat its muffled drum,
Lowly, lowly:
May the passing moments roll
Bliss eternal to thy soul,

Holy, holy!
Holy, holy.
Once I loved thee, Mary dear,
O how truly!
Once I loved thee, Mary dear,
O how truly!

The Village Maiden

If one were to sing only the first verse of this song, he would think that it was an altogether happy lyric about a lovely bride. While the music remains the same in the second and third verses, the words go from bad to worse. In the second verse the heroine is troubled by some terrible grief, and in the third she has succumbed to sorrow and the choir is singing her requiem.

Probably unaware of the romantic movement which was sweeping over Europe, Foster was nonetheless a child of his time and somehow felt the currents of the sentimentalism which engulfed the writers and musicians of all nations. It became almost the world fashion to sing of sorrow and death with longing and anticipation. A wedding inevitably suggested a requiem; hearts were overladen and hopes were flown.

Foster really had actual reasons for sadness at the time *The Village Maiden* was written. His father and mother had died within six months of each other.

The Village Maiden was published in September of 1855, a few months after *Come Where My Love Lies Dreaming* was issued.

1. The vil - lage bells are
2. But sum - mer joys have

ring - ing, And mer - ri - ly they chime; The vil - lage choir is
fad - ed And sum - mer hopes have flown; Her brow with grief is

sing - ing, For 'tis a hap - py time; The chap - el walls are
shad - ed, Her hap - py smiles are gone; Yet why her heart is

cresc.

lad - en With gar - lands rich and gay, To greet the vil - lage
lad - en, Not one, a - las! can say, Who saw the vil - lage

dim.

maid - en Up - on her wed - ding day.
maid - en Up - on her wed - ding day.

3

The village bells are ringing,
But hark, how sad and slow,
The village choir is singing
A requiem soft and low;
And all with sorrow laden
Their tearful tribute pay
Who saw the village maiden
Upon her wedding day.

Under the Willow She's Sleeping

The willow has been a symbol of mourning since the sixteenth century, and it appeared as a token of death or as an emblem of being forsaken in dozens of nineteenth-century songs. Stephen Foster was following the fashion when he wrote this song of a mother weeping over the grave of her child. *Under the Willow She's Sleeping* was published in 1860 by Firth, Pond & Company.

Even though he adopted the then fashionable practice of writing songs that tugged at the heartstrings, Foster was expressing his own mournful spirit. He might use the prevailing clichés but he most often imbued them with a personal feeling that was as genuine as it was appealing. Such songs as *Under the Willow She's Sleeping* are certainly characteristic of Foster's time, but they also were a striving to satisfy his own craving for comfort and understanding. They explain Stephen Foster quite as clearly as do the joyous songs of happier moods.

1. Un - der the wil low she's laid with care,
2. Un - der the wil low no songs are heard,

[179]

(Sang a lone moth-er while weep-ing,)— Un-der the wil-low, with

Near where my dar-ling lies dream ing;— Nought but the voice of some

gold - en hair, My lit - tle one's qui-et-ly sleep-ing.—

far - off bird Where life and its pleas ures are beam-ing.—

Chorus

mf Fair, fair, and gold - en hair; p (Sang a lone moth er while weep ing,)—

Fair, fair, and gold - en hair; (Sang a lone moth-er while weep-ing,)—

cresc.

dim.

Fair,   fair,   and   gold - en hair;   Un - der the wil - low she's sleep ing.

Fair,   fair,   and   gold - en hair;   Un - der the wil - low she's sleep ing.

3

Under the willow by night and day,
Sorrowing ever I ponder;
Free from its shadowy, gloomy ray,
Ah! never again can she wander.

4

Under the willow I breathe a prayer,
Longing to linger forever
Near to my angel with golden hair,
In lands where there's sorrowing never.

Why Have My Loved Ones Gone?

Self-pity songs were highly popular in the nineteenth century, and the fashion has by no means disappeared with twentieth-century sophistication. Stephen Foster was merely conforming to the style when he composed songs of this type. *Why Have My Loved Ones Gone?* is distinctly a self-pity song, with its hero longing for the death which has relieved his friends of their troubles, but which has left him to suffer, and to moan. Foster's song was published in 1861.

Songs of this genre were in a very real sense the "torch songs" of the Civil War decade and for a considerable time thereafter. Musically they were wholly unlike the "blues songs" of our day which tell of lovers vanishing. Yet Foster's self-pity songs voice fundamentally the same emotions. They differ, however, in being always tender and inoffensive. In Foster's time it would have been unthinkable to flaunt sex frustrations as brazenly as do the "blues songs" heard nowadays in night clubs.

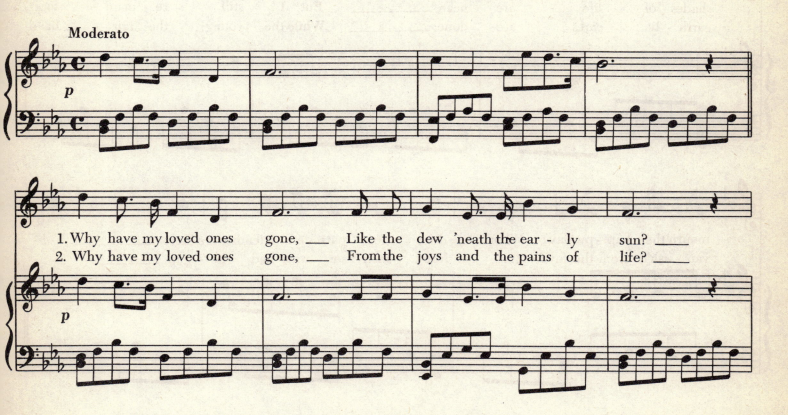

Moderato

1. Why have my loved ones gone, ___ Like the dew 'neath the ear - ly sun? ___
2. Why have my loved ones gone, ___ From the joys and the pains of life? ___

Why am I left a - lone, _____ While all their trou -bles here are
Why do I still live on, _____ A - lone to bat -tle in the

done? _____ My days of youth have passed a - way _____ And the
strife? _____ A - lone to strug -gle in the fray, _____ Till my

shades of life are near, _____ But I still re -main to
earth -ly cares are done; _____ While the young, the fair have

mourn the hap -py days When dear de -part -ed friends were here. _____
van - ish'd from the day, Be - fore their sor -rows had be - gun. _____

Chorus

Why have my lov'd ones gone, ———— Gone to re-turn no more———— Calm - ly glid - ing o'er a Sum -mer sea Whilst I'm left plod -ding on the shore? ————

3

Why have my loved ones gone,
While the springtime is on the breeze?
Gilding the hillside farm,
And breathing music thro' the trees!
The birds are singing in the air,
And the flow'rs are in their bloom;
All things around are beautiful and fair,
But still my spirit lies in gloom.

[185]

I Will Be True to Thee

This song was published in 1862, during the New York years. For most of his songs during this period, Stephen collaborated with lyric-writers and did not often write his own verses. *I Will Be True to Thee* is an exception, but not too good a one, for it indulges in morbid self-pity. The music of the song is superior to the words, and superior also to the music of most of the songs Foster composed in his last years.

Fidelity was a virtue often celebrated in song. It was a sentiment certain to be popularly approved by friends gathered around a piano. Depressed and groping for new ideas at this time, Foster strained now to write verses that are as tortured as they are lacking in felicity. It is possible that the visit of his wife and daughter to New York and their subsequent parting under unhappy circumstances forced him into this declaration of devotion. This feeling continued even though circumstances and temperaments made it impossible for Stephen and Jane to live together.

thee, _____ Though I share in thy worst des - pair, _____
thee, _____ Though I roam in a far off land, _____

I will be true to thee, _____ Though my own heart be bowed with
Wheth - er on earth or sea, _____ In a bow - er or de - sert

care. _____ Though cold neg - lect up - on thy hopes may fall, Though
strand, _____ Though dark - est clouds may mar the morn - ing beams, And

fears of death may hov - er near thy soul, Though fu - ner - al knells up -
va - pors dull may set - tle on the streams, Though blight - ing Time de -

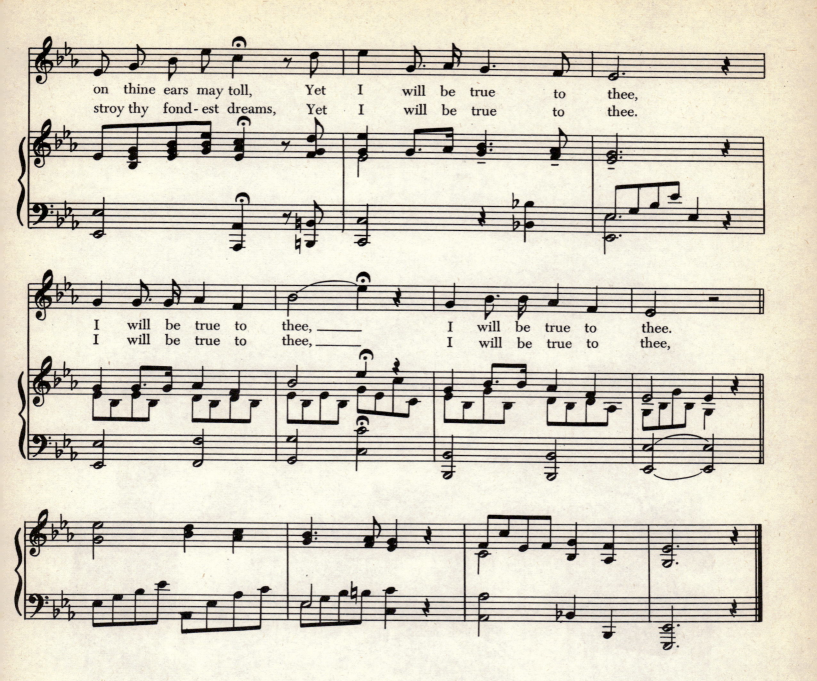

on thine ears may toll, Yet I will be true to thee,
stroy thy fond-est dreams, Yet I will be true to thee.

I will be true to thee, ____ I will be true to thee.
I will be true to thee, ____ I will be true to thee,

3

I will be true to thee;
   I will pray for thee night and day;
Wilt thou be true to me,
   As in years that have rolled away?
When all thy childhood's dearest hopes have
   fled
And gloomy visions linger round thy head,
When all thy dear and early friends are
   dead,
     Then I will be true to thee.
     I will be true to thee,
     I will be true to thee.

Why, No One to Love?

Although Foster occasionally followed the popular fashion by writing self-pity songs, he showed his scorn for moody introspection by composing an answer-song to a mournful ballad written by Ellen Clementine and M. H. Frank, entitled *No One to Love*. "What have you done in this beautiful world, that you're sighing of no one to love?" asked Foster, in a song called: *Why, No One to Love?*

Even in his last years, the mood of despair could not be altogether constant with Foster.

In this period, he showed his resilience by throwing off the black habit of despondency and writing songs that decried the wail of hopelessness. Here the writing is fresh and spontaneous; it does not depend upon the stencils and stock items of the period. It insists that there is a brighter world by declaring:

Many a fair one that dwells on the earth
Who would greet you with kind words of cheer,
Many who gladly would join in your pleasures
Or share in your grief with a tear.

1. No one to love in this beau-ti-ful
2. Dark is the soul that has noth-ing to

world, Full of warm hearts and bright beam-ing eyes? _____
dwell on! How sad must its bright-est hours prove! _____

Where is the lone heart that noth-ing can find That is love-ly be-
Lone-ly the dull brood-ing spir-it must be That has no one to

neath the blue skies. _____ No one to love! _____
cher-ish and love. _____ No one to love! _____

No one to love! ___ Why ___ no one to love? _____
No one to love! ___ Why ___ no one to love? _____

What have you done in this beau - ti - ful world, That you're sigh - ing of

What have you done in this beau - ti - ful world, That you're sigh - ing of

no one to love? _____

no one to love? _____

3

Many a fair one that dwells on the earth
Who would greet you with kind words of
    cheer,
Many who gladly would join in your pleas-
    ures
Or share in your grief with a tear.
    No one to love!
    No one to love!
    Why no one to love?
Where have you roamed in this beautiful
    world
That you're sighing of no one to love?

Some Folks

Here is another pleasant answer to the mournful, self-pity songs which were so popular in the nineteenth century, and which Foster himself sometimes wrote. *Some Folks* is a song of smiles and laughter, and it deserves to be more widely sung than it was in Foster's time, or than it is today. It was published by Firth, Pond & Company on the same day that the firm issued *Come Where My Love Lies Dreaming*, June 28, 1855.

In its spirit this song is almost like an English madrigal. It is a pity that Stephen Foster in his later years could not have heeded the admonition he had given just a half dozen years before to those who like to sigh, who long to die, who fear to smile, who fret and scold and who otherwise let themselves grow gray with brooding.

The public of Foster's day responded with mild enthusiasm to his exhortation for cheerfulness. At any rate, in the first year and a half three thousand persons bought this song, according to Foster's royalty records.

1. Some folks like to sigh,
2. Some folks fear to smile,

Some folks do, some folks do; Some folks long to
Some folks do, some folks do; Oth - ers laugh through

die, But that's not me nor you.
guile, But that's not me nor you.

Chorus Vivace

Long live the mer - ry, mer - ry heart That laughs by night and

day, Like the Queen of Mirth, No mat - ter what some folks

say.

3

Some folks fret and scold,
Some folks do, some folks do;
They'll soon be dead and cold,
But that's not me nor you.

4

Some folks get gray hairs,
Some folks do, some folks do;
Brooding o'er their cares,
But that's not me nor you.

5

Some folks toil and save,
Some folks do, some folks do,
To buy themselves a grave,
But that's not me nor you.

Sweetly She Sleeps, My Alice Fair

Here is another song which depicts a young lady asleep, and not departed from this world. *Sweetly She Sleeps* is a truly beautiful ballad, and it provided the late John McCormack with material for one of the most exquisite phonograph records he ever made. But in spite of its loveliness, it has been lamentably unappreciated and neglected. First issued by F. D. Benteen of Baltimore, March 18, 1851, it earned for Foster only $5.62 in royalties in the ensuing six years.

Sweetly She Sleeps is also a further example of those parallels with other musical compositions which delight those who make a business of tracing song origins. The first phrase of the song is melodically similar to that of a hymn-tune composed by Richard Storrs Willis for Edmund H. Sears' Christmas Carol, *It Came Upon the Midnight Clear.* Foster's song and Willis's hymn-tune were published in the same year; so it is not certain that either composer had heard the other's melody. The words of Foster's song were written by Charles G. Eastman. For the most part, Foster wrote the words as well as the music for his songs. It was not uncommon for him to use poems of others, and they represent the wide variety of his reading taste.

Al - ice fair, Her cheek on the pil - low pressed, ____
Al - ice fair, Her cheek like the first May rose, ____

Sweet - ly she sleeps, while her Sax - on hair, Like sun - light, streamso'er her
Sweet - ly she sleeps, ___ and all her care Is for - got - ten in soft re -

breast. _____ Hush! Let her sleep! I pray, sweet breeze, Breathe
pose. _____ Hush! though the ear - liest beams of light Their

low on the ma - ple bough _____ Hush! ___ bright bird, on her
wings in the blue sea dip, _____ Let her sleep, ___ I pray, while her

win-dow trees! For sweet-ly she sleep eth now.____ Sweet-ly she sleeps, my
dreams are bright, And a smile is a-bout her lip.____ Sweet-ly she sleeps, my

Al - ice fair, Her cheek on the pil-low pressed.____
Al - ice fair, Her cheek on the pil-low pressed,____

Sweet-ly she sleeps, while her Sax - on hair, Like sun-light,streams o'er her breast.____
Sweet-ly she sleeps, while her Sax - on hair, Like sun-light,streams o'er her breast.____

I Would Not Die in Springtime

This is the first of a series of songs. It was published in 1850 under the authorship of "Milton Moore," which was a nom de plume of Foster's, made from the names of John Milton and Thomas Moore. A year later another song was issued: *I Would Not Die in Summertime,* now under Foster's own name. In the same year a third season was represented by a song attributed to "J. H. Milton," *I Would Not Die in Winter,* and it seems reasonable to suspect that Stephen was again the author. Why Autumn was neglected may only be surmised, but it may have been because a contemporary songwriter, John Hill Hewitt, put an end to the whole business in 1852 by publishing a song entitled: *I Would Not Die At All.*

Apparently Spring was a more popular season with Foster's audience than Summer. *I Would Not Die in Springtime* and *I Would Not Die in Summertime* were both published by F. D. Benteen of Baltimore, one in 1850 and the other in 1851. In the period from publication to the time Foster made his total summary of royalties, in 1857, the song about Spring earned $78.12, and the Summer ballad only $11.26. Unfortunately, the success of the Winter song, if it was actually written by Foster, cannot be estimated, because it does not appear on his lists of earnings. And still more unfortunately, we have no way of knowing how the public responded to Hewitt's assurance that he would not die at all.

Spring time When all is bright a - round, And
Sum - mer When mu - sic's on the breeze, And

fair young flowers are peep - ing From out the si - lent
soft, de - li - cious mur - murs Float ev - er through the

ground, When life is on the wa - ter And joy up - on the
trees, And fair - y birds are sing - ing From morn till close of

shore; For win - ter, gloom - y win - ter Then reigns o'er us no
day— No: with its tran - sient glo - ries I would not pass a -

more.
way.

3

When breezes leave the mountain,
Its balmy sweets all o'er—
To breathe around the fountain
And fan our bowers no more.
When Summer flowers are dying
Within the lonely glen,
And Autumn winds are sighing—
I would not perish then.

4

But let me die in Winter
When night hangs dark above,
And cold the snow is lying
On bosoms that we love—
Ah! may the wind at midnight,
That bloweth from the sea,
Chant mildly, softly, sweetly
A requiem for me.

If You've Only Got a Moustache

A forerunner of the type of song which achieved great popularity in the English music halls, *If You've Only Got a Moustache*, with words by George Cooper, represents a satire of fashion always sure to win an audience. Songs of this sort are historically valuable as a record of the clothes and affectations of the dandies of each period. Of course the handlebar moustache of the day before yesterday was a far more formidable affair than the hemstitched line on the upper lip of our own motion-picture idols or the little brush copied from Charlie Chaplin by the late, unlamented Adolf Hitler.

Foster's few songs in this vein, totally different from the nonsense songs which he wrote so successfully for the minstrel shows, actually anticipated the kind of song brought from England by such comedians as William Horace Lingard, who came to America only a few years after Foster's death. He, too, satirized fashions of the day, most notably in *The Grecian Bend*, of which he wrote only the words.

all of you poor sin - gle men _____ Don't ev - er give up in de -
mat - ter for man - ners or style, _____ No mat - ter for birth or for

spair, For there's al - ways a chance while there's life _____ To
fame, All these used to have some - thing to do _____ With

cap - ture the hearts of the fair. _____ No mat - ter what may be your
young la - dies chang - ing their name. _____ There's no rea - son now to de -

age, _____ You al - ways may cut a fine dash, _____ You will
spond, _____ Or go and do an - y - thing rash, _____ For you'll

suit all the girls to a hair _____ If you've on- ly got a mous-
do though you can't raise a cent, _____ If you'll on- ly raise a mous-

tache! A mous- tache, a mous- tache! If you've on- ly got a moustache! A mous- tache, a mous- tache, If you'll on- ly raise a mous-

tache. _____
tache. _____

3

Your head may be thick as a block,
And empty as any foot-ball,
Oh! your eyes may be green as the grass,
Your heart just as hard as a wall.
Yet take the advice that I give,
You'll soon gain affection and cash,
And will be all the rage with the girls,
If you'll only get a moustache,
    A moustache, a moustache,
      If you'll only get a moustache.

4

I once was in sorrow and tears
Because I was jilted you know,
So right down to the river I ran
To quickly dispose of my woe.
A good friend he gave me advice
And timely prevented the splash.
Now at home I've a wife and ten heirs,
And all through a handsome moustache,
    A moustache, a moustache,
      And all through a handsome mous-
        tache.

Mr. & Mrs. Brown

This is another of the later Foster songs which were not typical of the minstrel shows, but rather of the music-hall. Shortly after Foster's death they were popularized by such English comedians as William Horace Lingard and George Leybourne, who is supposed to have written the words for *The Man on the Flying Trapeze*.

Unlike *If You've Only Got a Moustache*, *Mr. & Mrs. Brown* does not satirize fashions of the day. It deals, rather, with a too well-known family contretemps in which the husband arrives home considerably after two o'clock in

the morning. The song is in five verses, for which there is space for only three. First, there is an argument about the accuracy of the clock. Then the wife inquires where the husband has been and with whom he is consorting. The situation becomes complicated, but it all ends peacefully.

It is a rather touching commentary that Stephen Foster, whose matrimonial history was tragic, could write in so light a vein, to the words of George Cooper which dealt with the vagaries of married life.

She.

So Mis - ter Brown, you've come at last, I'm sure it's af - ter two.

He.
Dear Mistress Brown, your clock is fast, I know as well as you.

She.
Oh! Sir, it's shameful, so it is, Don't come, sir, in my sight!

He.
Now give me one good kiss to-night, You see that I'm all right.

She.
I cannot talk to you to-night, I see that you're not right. Oh!

He.
Now give me one good kiss to-night, You see that I'm all right. Oh!

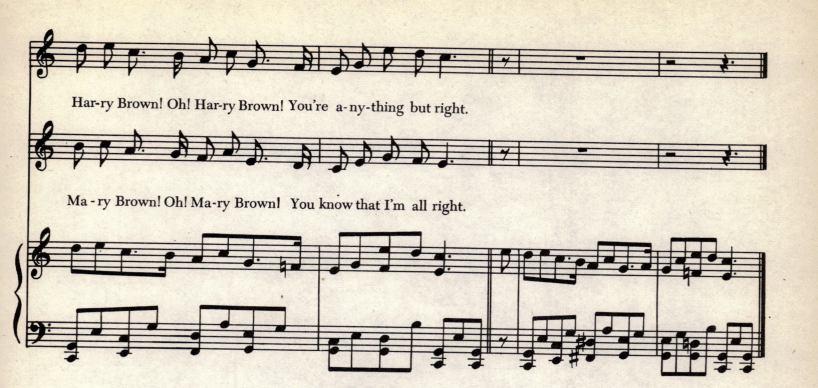

Har-ry Brown! Oh! Har-ry Brown! You're a-ny-thing but right.

Ma - ry Brown! Oh! Ma-ry Brown! You know that I'm all right.

2

SHE. All right! you good for nothing you,
        Have I not eyes to see?
HE. No Madam, what I say is true,
        I'm only on a spree!
SHE. Don't make me angry, Mr. Brown,
        For if you do I'll cry!
HE. I shall not stay to see you frown,
        So, Mrs. Brown, good-bye.
HE. { I shall not stay to see you frown,
BOTH. {   So, Mrs. Brown, good-bye.
SHE. { I'll make you stay to see me frown,
     {   You shall not say good-bye.
HE. { O! Mary Brown, O! Mary Brown,
BOTH. {   I'll have to say good-bye.
SHE. { O! Harry Brown, O! Harry Brown,
    {   You see you've made me cry.

3. SHE. *Furiously.*

Hard hearted man, I tell you what,
    I must know where you've been;
I am not jealous, O! no! no!
    But it's a shame and sin!
Your bosom friend, young Jones, just left,
    He calls here every night,
I'm sure if it were not for him
    I'd really die with fright.
SHE. { I'm sure if it were not for him,
BOTH. {   I'd really die with fright.
HE. { What Ma'am, if it were not for him
   {   You say you'd die with fright!
HE. { O! Mary Brown, O! Mary Brown,
BOTH. {   I'll call him out to fight!
SHE. { O! Harry Brown, O! Harry Brown,
   {   He's far above your height.

Wilt Thou Be Gone, Love?

Like *Come Where My Love Lies Dreaming*, *Wilt Thou Be Gone, Love?* is an attempt at writing a "composed-through" song. It was published in 1851 as a "vocal duett," "subject from Shakespeare's Romeo and Juliet." The words were adapted by Foster from the lines spoken by Juliet and Romeo at the beginning of Scene 5, Act 3. Juliet says she hears a nightingale and Romeo insists that it is a lark.

Foster was devoted to reading and his taste was discriminating. He had a great fondness for the writings of Edgar Allan Poe, with whom he was temperamentally akin. In the inside cover of his manuscript book there appears a list of books which he evidently had purchased. Carefully noted are the prices he had paid for them. Dickens' *Bleak House* heads the list, at sixty cents. Scott, Cowper, Maryatt were represented, at fifty, twenty-five and forty cents, respectively. He indulged himself to the amount of two dollars for a Webster's dictionary.

Wilt thou be gone,____ wilt thou be gone, love, gone love, from

me? Stay! 'tis the Night - in - gale that sings in yon - der

tree._____ Deem not 'tis the Lark, love; day is not yet

near_____ Be - lieve me, 'tis the Night - in - gale whose song hath pierced thine

ear. Wilt thou be gone, wilt thou be gone, ___ love, wilt
Romeo.

I must be gone, ___ love, I

a tempo

thou be gone from me? _____ Stay! 'tis the Night - in - gale that

must be gone from thee. _____ 'Tis not the Night - in - gale that

sings in yon - der tree. _____ Love, 'tis the Night - in - gale,

sings in yon - der tree. 'Tis the Lark, 'tis the

love, 'tis the Night - in - gale, love, 'tis the Night - in - gale that

Lark 'tis the Lark, 'Tis the Lark, love, that

rit.

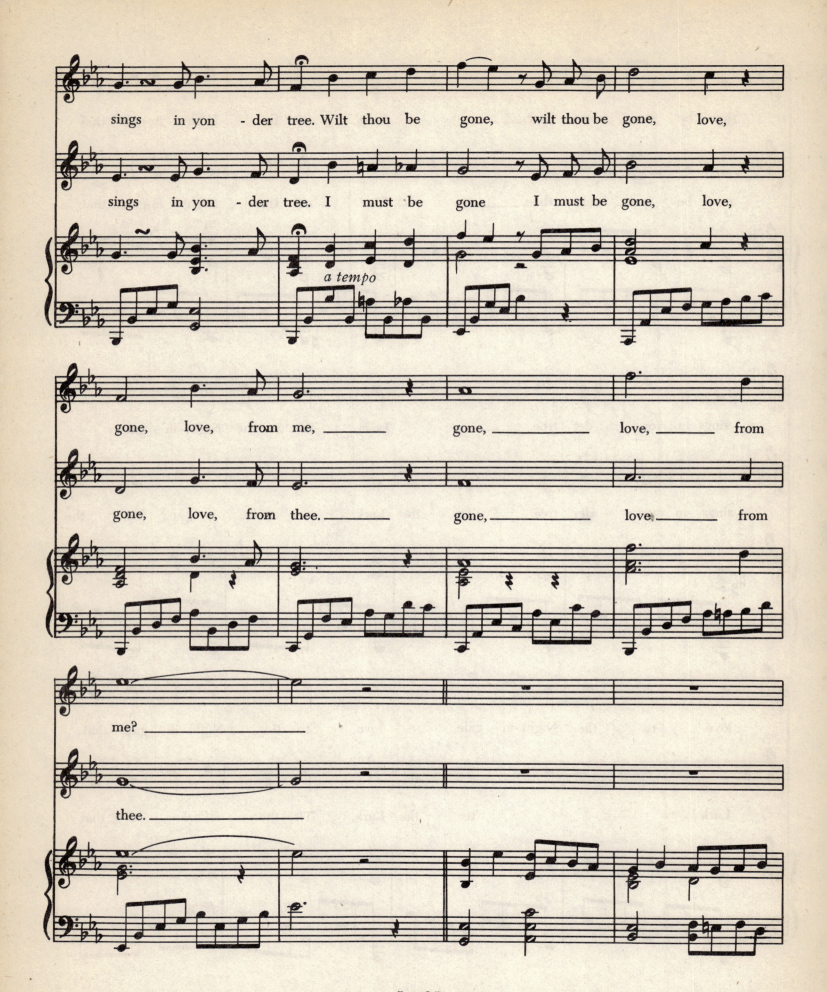

sings in yon - der tree. Wilt thou be gone, wilt thou be gone, love,

sings in yon - der tree. I must be gone I must be gone, love,

a tempo

gone, love, from me, _____ gone, _____ love, _____ from

gone, love, from thee. _____ gone, _____ love _____ from

me? _____

thee. _____

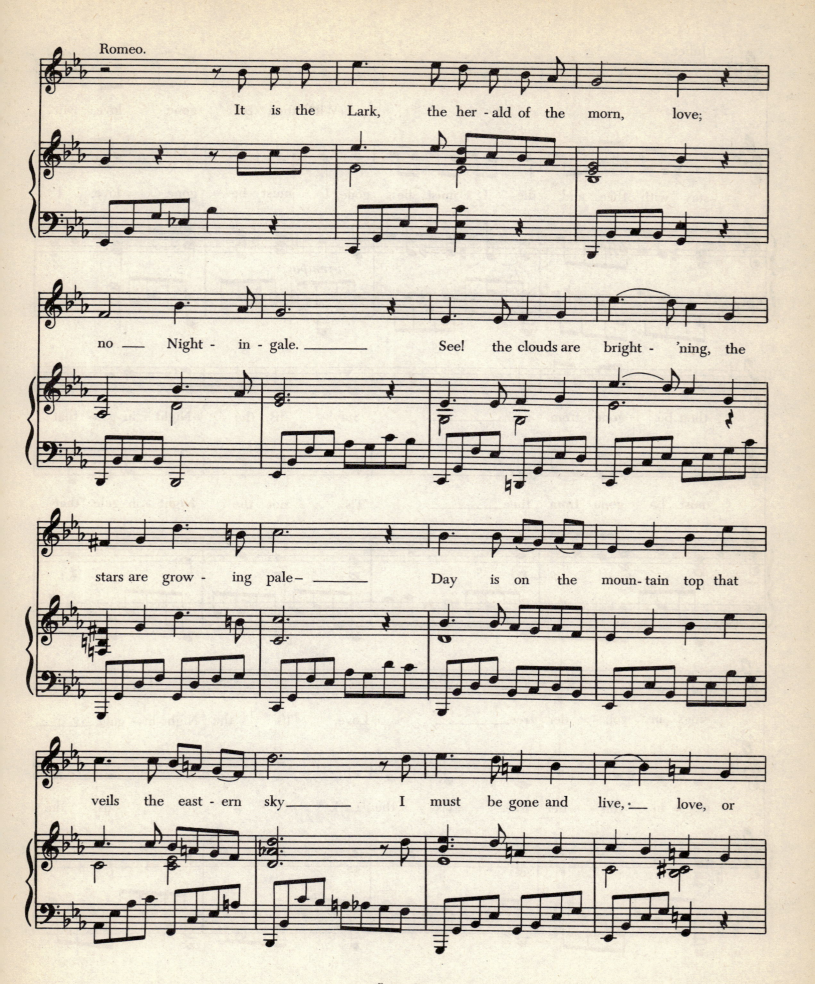

Romeo.

It is the Lark, the her-ald of the morn, love; no — Night - in - gale. _____ See! the clouds are bright - 'ning, the

stars are grow - ing pale— _____ Day is on the moun-tain top that

veils the east - ern sky _____ I must be gone and live, — love, or

love,   'tis   the Night-in-gale, _____ love,   'tis   the   Night-in-gale that

Lark, _____   'tis   the   Lark,   'tis   the   Lark, _ love, that

rit.

sings   in yon - der tree. _____   Wilt thou be   gone,   wilt thou be

sings   in yon - der tree. _____   I   must be   gone,   I   must be

a tempo

gone, _ love, _____ wilt   thou be   gone, love, from me? _____

gone, _ love, _____   I   must be   gone, love, from thee. _____

a tempo